Addition and Subtraction

Beyond Math Facts

Susan Greenwald, M.A. Ed.

LONGEVITY PUBLISHING
Englewood, Colorado • www.LongevityPublishing.com

This book has been a labor of love
for students of all ages,
and will continue to be beneficial
for as long as children learn mathematics.

For Madison Olivia and Morgan Harper, with love.

Addition and Subtraction:
Beyond Math Facts
LP 250

Longevity Publishing
Englewood, Colorado
www.LongevityPublishing.com
ISBN: 978-0-9777323-2-6
10 9 8 7 6 5 4 3 2

First printing 2012

Edited by: Susan Hindman, Wordwise Editing
Design by: DBS, Inc.
Cover Design by: Lee Lewis Walsh, Words Plus Design

Table of Contents

Introduction

Addition and Subtraction: Beyond Math Facts (LP 250) is a practical resource workbook. **Six sections of workbook pages** provide students with structured addition and subtraction on a level beyond math facts.

Designed for any age student, *Addition and Subtraction: Beyond Math Facts* helps students master **two-, three-, and four-digit addition and subtraction, with and without regrouping**.

The 55 reproducible practice pages are suitable for:
- Children needing **instruction**, **practice**, or **review** of addition and subtraction with larger numbers
- Children in accelerated programs
- Children in remedial programs
- Children with math disabilities
- Older students who are still learning math facts

Knowledge and fluency of math facts is essential for success and proficiency in computation skills, and for solving real-life math problems.

If you are using this book and *Two Plus Two Is Not Five: Easy Methods to Learn Addition and Subtraction* (LP 200), you will find that the sequence in which the math facts are introduced is the same.

- **Six sections of practice problems** allow students to review a different group of addition and subtraction facts, as they learn how to add and subtract with two-, three-, and four-digit problems.
- Once introduced, the addition and subtraction facts are used throughout the book.
- **Addition and subtraction are practiced together** on nearly all the pages.

Pages are arranged in a format that is useful to ★ resource room teachers, ★ classroom teachers, ★ home schooling educators, ★ parents, and ★ tutors.

- **Pre- and Post-Assessments** and a **Record-Keeping Chart** are provided.
- The **Guide to Teaching the Lessons** is easy to use.
- Lessons can be easily individualized for different learning abilities.
- Most of the practice pages are divided into two sections so that half sheets can be assigned.
- Each section includes a **Word Math** page.

Experienced teachers can choose to start on page 1 or with the **Pre-Assessment** on **page 57**.

Otherwise, read **How to Use This Book** and then the **Guide to Teaching the Lessons**.

Enjoy teaching math!
Susan Greenwald, M.A. Ed.

How to Use This Book

Addition and Subtraction: Beyond Math Facts (LP 250) introduces adding and subtracting larger numbers. Students will add and subtract with two-, three-, and four-digit numbers, and learn place values beyond tens and ones.

Phrases such as "one ten" and "three hundreds" are written as "1 ten" and "3 hundreds," respectively. The words "ones, tens, hundreds, and thousands," when used to explain place value, are written "1's, 10's, 100's, and 1000's."

Where to Begin
Refer to **these instructions** and the **Guide to Teaching the Lessons**.

- For beginners, skip the **Pre-Assessment**, and start with the instructions on page vii.
- If students have had experience working with two or more digit numbers, have them complete the **Pre-Assessment** on **pages 57 and 58**. Use this test to get a baseline of knowledge. If students need to count to get answers, ask them to place a dot above any problem where they had to count. Begin with the page number indicated on the **Record-Keeping Chart** (see below) where a student did not get all the problems correct.

Differentiate
The workbook is designed to be used in sequence, but encourages curriculum compacting. If students mastered a particular skill, you can choose to do some review, assign fewer practice problems, or advance them by skipping to those skills needing instruction.

> **It is important to look at what kinds of errors students are making.**
> - If math facts are not memorized, are children counting incorrectly to get answers?
> - Are careless errors made because columns are not straight?
> - Is a student proficient with math facts but unfamiliar with regrouping?
> - Is a student regrouping a new ten or hundred, but placing it in the wrong spot and therefore calculating incorrectly?

Record-Keeping
Each problem on the **Pre- and Post-Assessment** pages has a letter. Mark the **Record-Keeping Chart** on **page 56** by finding the matching letters and filling in a box for each correct answer. Then mark the total score. Make a notation if the student needed to count for an answer.

Date and record progress as skills are introduced and mastered. Assign the **Post-Assessment** on **pages 59 and 60** after completion of the book.

> For those students who first need to learn basic addition and subtraction facts, I suggest starting with *Two Plus Two Is Not Five: Easy Methods to Learn Addition and Subtraction* (LP 200). Have the students complete Tier 1 of *Two Plus Two Is Not Five*, then begin page 1 of this book.

Teaching Regrouping

> • **Regrouping in addition** refers to the *exchange or trade* of 10 ones for a new ten, 10 tens for a new hundred, or 10 hundreds for a new thousand. (You may know of this by another phrase: to "*carry*" a number to the next place.)
>
> • **Regrouping in subtraction** refers to the *exchange or trade* of 1 ten for 10 ones, 1 hundred for 10 tens, or 1 thousand for 10 hundreds. (You may know of this by the phrase: to "*borrow*" from a number.)

A place value chart such as this allows students to see and understand why we **regroup**.

Place Value Chart

Hundreds	Tens	Ones

To introduce the new lessons, use

   * a place value chart
   * the words *regroup, exchange,* and *trade*
   * drawings of cubes or actual cubes to demonstrate representation of addition and subtraction

Continue to do so with a few problems, then allow students to complete the pages.

Word Math

Meaningful, real-life word problems help children see reasons for learning new math skills and assist in the **transfer of those skills to solving real-life math problems**. Students should have some previous instruction with word math vocabulary.

Money

Addition and subtraction with money is introduced on page 32. The purpose is to transfer new computation skills to working with money.

Guide to Teaching the Lessons

Listed below with each section is a set of math facts. These are the facts that will be used in that section. Once facts are introduced, they will be reviewed throughout the book.

SECTION 1 (Pages 1–8)
Math facts: 1+1, 1+2, 2+1, 1+3, 3+1, 1+4, 4+1, 1+5, 5+1, 1+6, 6+1, 1+7, 7+1, 1+8, 8+1, 1+9, 9+1; 2+4, 4+2, 2+6, 6+2, 2+8, 8+2; 2+2, 3+3, 4+4, 5+5; 10−5, 8−4, 6−3, 4−2; 10−1, 9−1, 8−1, 7−1, 6−1, 5−1, 4−1, 3−1, 2−1; 10−9, 9−8, 8−7, 7−6, 6−5, 5−4, 4−3, 3−2; number + zero, and zero + a number.

Page 1: Adding two- and one-digit numbers. No regrouping.

☞ **TIP:** Remember to use meaningful **real-life word math problems** when introducing new lessons. **Example:** There are 71 children and five teachers in the second-grade classes. How many people in all?

Use a **place value chart** to show 71 as 7 tens and 1 one. Ask your students to add on 5 more ones. First, count the 7 tens: 10, 20, 30, 40, 50, 60, 70. Then add on the ones: 71, 72, 73, 74, 75, 76.

Next, do the math on paper for **71+5**. Remember to do this with a few more problems. Then allow students to complete the page.

☞ **TIP:** Instruct students to add or subtract numbers in the 1's column first. 1+5=6. Then bring the 7 down to the answer space, as there are no other numbers in the 10's column to add. (7+0=7)

$$\begin{array}{r} 71 \\ +\ 5 \\ \hline 6 \end{array} \qquad \begin{array}{r} 71 \\ +\ 5 \\ \hline 76 \end{array}$$

Page 2: Subtracting with two- and one-digit numbers. No regrouping.
Refer to page 1 instructions above.

Page 3: Addition and subtraction practice. No regrouping.
SUGGESTION: Call attention to the mix of addition and subtraction signs on this practice page.

Page 4: Adding and subtracting with two-digit numbers. No regrouping.
Use a place value chart to show **61+25**. Do the same for **42−31 in row D**.

$$\begin{array}{r} 61 \\ +25 \\ \hline 86 \end{array} \qquad \begin{array}{r} 42 \\ -31 \\ \hline 11 \end{array}$$

ADDITION REGROUPING:
- Use counting cubes to show how 10 cubes will not fit in either the 1's, 10's, or 100's place.
- Note that not all the practice problems require regrouping.

Pages 7–8: Adding two- and one-digit numbers.
Regrouping to the 10's place, and subtraction practice.
Show 27+1 and 28+1. There is no need to regroup. Next, show **29+1**. The 10 cubes will not fit in the 1's place space. To add 9+1, explain that the 10 ones are regrouped for 1 new ten. Place the new ten in the 10's place. Now there are 3 tens, or 30, and zero ones.

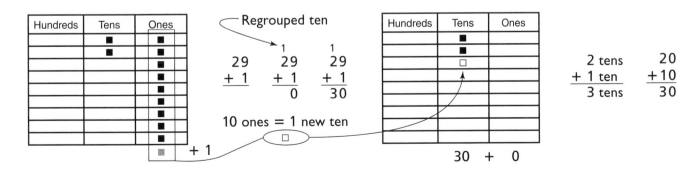

Next, do the math on paper.

☞ **TIP:** Remind students to add the numbers in the 1's column first, and to show a new ten by writing a tiny numeral 1 at the top of the 10's column. Then add the tens.

SECTION 2 (Pages 9–16)

Math facts include: 2+3, 3+2, 3+4, 4+3; 3+5, 5+3, 4+6, 6+4; 6+6, 7+7, 12−6, 14−7; 2+9, 9+2, 3+9, 9+3, 4+9, 9+4, 5+9, 9+5, 6+9, 9+6, 7+9, 9+7, 8+9, 9+8, 9+9; number − number; and number − zero.

SUBTRACTION REGROUPING:

- Use counting cubes to show that sometimes there are not enough in a column to subtract.
- Note that not all the practice problems require regrouping.

Pages 11–12: Subtracting with two- and one-digit numbers.
Regrouping from the 10's place, and addition practice.

Show 79−8 and 41−1. There is no need to regroup. Next, show **30−1**. Ask students to subtract, or take away, 1 one from the 1's place, where there are no ones. Ask, "How can we get some ones?" Direct the students to remove one of the tens from the 10's place, and regroup it for 10 new ones. Place these 10 ones in the 1's place. Now there are enough ones to complete the subtraction. (10−1)

Next, do the math on paper.

☞ **TIP:** Show how to draw a line from **top left** to **bottom right** over the 3 in the 10's column. Write a tiny 1 next to the 0 to show the regrouped ten is now in the 1's column as 10 ones. Subtract 10−1. There were 3 tens, but 1 ten was taken to regroup for the new ones, so now there are only 2 tens. To show this, write a tiny 2 on top of the crossed-out number 3. Finally, bring this 2 down, as there are no other numbers in that column to subtract.

Work the next problem, **52−6**, using the same method. There are 2 ones in the 1's column, not enough to subtract 6. When 1 ten is regrouped from the 10's place for 10 new ones, there are a total of 12 ones. Write a tiny 1 next to the 2 to show the 12 ones, and subtract 12−6=6.

ADDITION AND SUBTRACTION USING THE 100's PLACE:

- With counting cubes, show a three-digit number as hundreds, tens, and ones.

Pages 15–16: Adding two-digit numbers. Regrouping to the 100's place, and subtraction practice.

Show 81+13. There is no need to regroup. Next, show **82+23**. Add the ones. Then add the tens: 8 tens + 2 tens = 10 tens, or 80+20=100. 10 tens will not fit in the 10's place space. Explain that 10 tens are regrouped for 1 new hundred. Place the new hundred in the 100's space. Now there are 1 hundred, zero tens, and 5 ones. Next, do the math on paper.

$$\begin{array}{r} 82 \\ +23 \\ \hline 5 \end{array} \qquad \begin{array}{r} 82 \\ +23 \\ \hline 105 \end{array}$$

Work the next problem **71+75** using the same method. 7 tens + 7 tens = 14 tens, or 70+70=140. 14 tens will not fit in the 10's place space. 10 tens are exchanged for 1 new hundred, and the remaining 4 tens stay in the 10's place.

$$\begin{array}{r} 71 \\ +75 \\ \hline 6 \end{array} \qquad \begin{array}{r} 71 \\ +75 \\ \hline 146 \end{array}$$

SECTION 3 (Pages 17–26)
Math facts include: 4+5, 5+4; 8+8, 16−8, 18−9; 5−2, 5−3, 7−3, 7−4; 10−2, 8−2, 6−2; 13−8, 13−5, 8−5, 5−3, 8+5, 5+8; 3+6, 6+3, 9−3, 9−6.

Page 19: Adding with three addends.
This skill prepares students to regroup from the 1's to 10's place when adding two-digit numbers. Direct students to use fact knowledge to see that **2+2+2** is 6, because 2+2=4 and 4+2=6. Show **3+3+2** is 8 because (3+3)+2 = 6+2=8. This can also be solved: 3+(3+2)=3+5=8.

Page 20: Adding two-digit numbers.
Regrouping to the 10's or 100's place, and subtraction practice.
Show **14+19**. Add: 4+9. 13 cubes will not fit in the 1's place space. Regroup 10 ones for 1 new ten, and 3 ones stay in the 1's place. Write a tiny numeral 1 at the top of the 10's column. Then add the tens: 1+1+1.

$$\text{Regrouped ten} \longrightarrow \begin{array}{r} 1 \\ 14 \\ +19 \\ \hline 33 \end{array}$$

Pages 23–24: Subtracting with two-digit numbers. Regrouping, and addition practice.
Review the process in subtraction to regroup 1 ten for 10 ones.

Page 25: Adding two-digit numbers. Two-place regrouping, and subtraction practice.
Show 64+19. Only the ones are regrouped. Next, show **12+99**. Review the process to regroup 10 ones for 1 ten, and 10 tens for 1 hundred.

SECTION 4 (Pages 27–35)
Math facts include: 5+7, 7+5, 6+8, 8+6; 4+7, 7+4, 11−4, 11−7; 9−4, 9−5; 17−8, 17−9, 16−7, 16−9, 15−6, 15−9, 14−5, 14−9, 13−4, 13−9, 12−3, 12−9, 11−2, 11−9.

Page 29: Adding and subtracting with three- and two-digit numbers.
Regrouping between the 10's and 1's places.
Review the process to regroup between the 10's and 1's places with three-digit numbers.

Pages 30–32: Adding three- and two-digit numbers. Subtraction regrouping from the 100's.
One-place regrouping. Show **416−73 in row D**.

$$\text{Regrouped hundred} \longrightarrow \begin{array}{r} {}^{3}4^{1}16 \\ -73 \\ \hline 343 \end{array}$$

Subtract the ones. Then subtract the tens. There is 1 ten, not enough to subtract 7. When 1 hundred is regrouped from the 100's place for 10 new tens, there are a total of 11 tens. Subtract 11−7. 11 tens − 7 tens = 4 tens, or 110−70=40. There are 3 hundreds remaining. Bring down that number 3. The answer is 343.

Note, **page 32** includes adding and subtracting with money to the **dollar** place.
SUGGESTION: Call attention to the money problems. The answers need dollar and cent signs.

Pages 33–34: Adding three- and two-digit numbers.
Two-place regrouping, and subtraction practice.
Show 244+94. Only the tens are regrouped. Next show 355+57. Review the process to regroup 10 ones for 1 ten, and 10 tens for 1 hundred.

SECTION 5 (Pages 36–44)
Math facts include: 5+6, 6+5, 6+7, 7+6, 7+8, 8+7; 2+5, 5+2, 7−2, 7−5; 2+7, 7+2, 9−2, 9−7; 4+8, 8+4, 12−4, 12−8; 10−8, 8−6, 6−4; 3+7, 7+3, 10−3, 10−7.

Pages 37–38: Subtracting with three- and two-digit numbers.
Two-place regrouping, and addition practice.
Show $958-19$ and $326-43$. Only one place is regrouped. Next, show $\textbf{634}-\textbf{67}$. Subtract the ones. There are not enough ones. Students need to first exchange 1 ten for 10 new ones for a total of 14 ones. Now $14-7$ can be completed. There are 2 tens remaining, not enough to subtract the 6 tens. Next, students need to exchange 1 hundred for 10 new tens for a total of 12 tens. Now $12-6$ can be completed. There are 5 hundreds remaining. Bring down that number 5.

Adding and subtracting with money starts in **row D on page 38**.

Pages 39–41: Adding and subtracting with three-digit numbers. One- and two-place regrouping.
These three-digit math problems review previously taught regrouping skills.

ADDITION AND SUBTRACTION WITH THE 1000's PLACE:
• With counting cubes, demonstrate what the numbers mean. Show digits of a four-digit number as thousands, hundreds, tens, and ones.
• Answers with four-digit numbers will include a comma between the hundreds and thousands.

☞ **TIP:** For answers resulting in more than 999, teach students to say: "1's, 10's, 100's, comma," and to place the comma at that point in front of 100's, to separate it from the 1000's place.

Pages 43–44: Adding three-digit numbers.
Three-place regrouping to the 1000's place, and subtraction practice.
Show $\textbf{835}+\textbf{251}$. Add the ones. Add the tens. Then show 8 hundreds + 2 hundreds = 10 hundreds or 1,000. The 10 cubes will not fit in the 100's place space. Remove 10 hundreds to regroup it for 1 new thousand. Place the new thousand in the 1000's space. Adding with money to the **ten-dollar** place starts in **Row D on page 44**.

Thousand	Hundreds	Tens	Ones
1 ,	0	8	6

$$\begin{array}{r} 835 \\ +\ 251 \\ \hline 1{,}086 \end{array}$$

SECTION 6 (Pages 45–55)
Math facts include: $3+8$, $8+3$, $11-3$, $11-8$; $10-4$, $10-6$, $12-5$, $12-7$, $14-6$, $14-8$; $11-5$, $11-6$, $13-6$, $13-7$, $15-7$, $15-8$.

Pages 49–50: Subtracting with three-digit numbers.
Two-place regrouping and zero, and addition practice.
Show $\textbf{905}-\textbf{118}$. Subtract the ones. Ask students to regroup 1 ten for 10 new ones when there are no tens. Direct students to first regroup 1 hundred for 10 new tens. Now there are enough tens to complete the exchange from tens to ones.

$$\begin{array}{ccccc}
\begin{array}{r}905\\-118\\\hline\end{array} &
\begin{array}{r}9\overset{1}{0}5\\-118\\\hline\end{array} &
\begin{array}{r}9\overset{1}{0}\overset{1}{5}\\-118\\\hline 7\end{array} &
\begin{array}{r}\overset{9}{\cancel{}}\ \\ 9\overset{1}{0}\overset{1}{5}\\-118\\\hline 87\end{array} &
\begin{array}{r}\overset{8\ \ 9}{\ }\\ 9\overset{1}{0}\overset{1}{5}\\-118\\\hline 787\end{array}
\end{array}$$

Pages 51–52: Adding and subtracting with four- and three-digit numbers. Three-place regrouping.
To teach regrouping with zero in the 100's place, refer to page 49 instructions above. Students will exchange 1 thousand for 10 new hundreds. Adding and subtracting with money to the **ten-dollar** place starts in **Row D on page 51**.

Pages 53–54: Adding and subtracting with four-digit numbers. Three-place regrouping.
Adding and subtracting with money to the **ten-dollar** place starts in **Row D on page 53**.

Name _____

Adding two- and one-digit numbers. No regrouping.

A.
71	42	24	2	67	94
+ 5	+ 1	+ 2	+ 8	+ 1	+ 4

B.
14	52	21	82	73	3
+ 1	+ 6	+ 3	+ 4	+ 0	+ 3

C.
8	26	60	9	5	31
+ 2	+ 1	+ 5	+ 1	+ 5	+ 8

D.
81	33	6	91	55	63
+ 7	+ 1	+ 2	+ 2	+ 1	+ 3

E.
61	10	51	2	18	1
+ 6	+ 8	+ 4	+ 4	+ 1	+ 9

F.
47	4	82	20	96	71
+ 0	+ 4	+ 2	+ 1	+ 2	+ 1

Addition and Subtraction: Beyond Math Facts   **1**

Name _____

Subtracting with two- and one-digit numbers. No regrouping.

A.
$$29 - 1 \quad 84 - 2 \quad 10 - 9 \quad 49 - 8 \quad 58 - 1 \quad 98 - 7$$

B.
$$6 - 5 \quad 77 - 1 \quad 26 - 3 \quad 13 - 2 \quad 10 - 1 \quad 25 - 4$$

C.
$$92 - 1 \quad 10 - 5 \quad 47 - 6 \quad 6 - 3 \quad 88 - 4 \quad 18 - 1$$

D.
$$74 - 2 \quad 53 - 1 \quad 36 - 5 \quad 15 - 1 \quad 84 - 3 \quad 4 - 2$$

E.
$$46 - 1 \quad 63 - 2 \quad 29 - 8 \quad 79 - 1 \quad 10 - 9 \quad 38 - 4$$

F.
$$10 - 5 \quad 55 - 4 \quad 63 - 1 \quad 96 - 3 \quad 34 - 1 \quad 78 - 7$$

Addition and Subtraction: Beyond Math Facts

Name _____

Addition and subtraction practice. No regrouping.

A.
$$\begin{array}{r} 34 \\ + 4 \\ \hline \end{array}$$
$$\begin{array}{r} 18 \\ - 7 \\ \hline \end{array}$$
$$\begin{array}{r} 86 \\ - 3 \\ \hline \end{array}$$
$$\begin{array}{r} 25 \\ - 1 \\ \hline \end{array}$$
$$\begin{array}{r} 91 \\ + 4 \\ \hline \end{array}$$
$$\begin{array}{r} 10 \\ - 9 \\ \hline \end{array}$$

B.
$$\begin{array}{r} 71 \\ + 8 \\ \hline \end{array}$$
$$\begin{array}{r} 22 \\ + 4 \\ \hline \end{array}$$
$$\begin{array}{r} 13 \\ - 1 \\ \hline \end{array}$$
$$\begin{array}{r} 92 \\ + 2 \\ \hline \end{array}$$
$$\begin{array}{r} 45 \\ - 4 \\ \hline \end{array}$$
$$\begin{array}{r} 11 \\ + 6 \\ \hline \end{array}$$

C.
$$\begin{array}{r} 65 \\ + 0 \\ \hline \end{array}$$
$$\begin{array}{r} 73 \\ + 1 \\ \hline \end{array}$$
$$\begin{array}{r} 39 \\ - 8 \\ \hline \end{array}$$
$$\begin{array}{r} 2 \\ + 8 \\ \hline \end{array}$$
$$\begin{array}{r} 53 \\ + 3 \\ \hline \end{array}$$
$$\begin{array}{r} 67 \\ - 6 \\ \hline \end{array}$$

D.
$$\begin{array}{r} 54 \\ - 2 \\ \hline \end{array}$$
$$\begin{array}{r} 30 \\ + 4 \\ \hline \end{array}$$
$$\begin{array}{r} 5 \\ + 5 \\ \hline \end{array}$$
$$\begin{array}{r} 94 \\ + 2 \\ \hline \end{array}$$
$$\begin{array}{r} 67 \\ - 1 \\ \hline \end{array}$$
$$\begin{array}{r} 41 \\ + 7 \\ \hline \end{array}$$

E.
$$\begin{array}{r} 42 \\ + 6 \\ \hline \end{array}$$
$$\begin{array}{r} 58 \\ - 4 \\ \hline \end{array}$$
$$\begin{array}{r} 10 \\ - 1 \\ \hline \end{array}$$
$$\begin{array}{r} 76 \\ - 5 \\ \hline \end{array}$$
$$\begin{array}{r} 8 \\ + 2 \\ \hline \end{array}$$
$$\begin{array}{r} 83 \\ - 2 \\ \hline \end{array}$$

F.
$$\begin{array}{r} 86 \\ - 1 \\ \hline \end{array}$$
$$\begin{array}{r} 1 \\ + 9 \\ \hline \end{array}$$
$$\begin{array}{r} 26 \\ + 2 \\ \hline \end{array}$$
$$\begin{array}{r} 59 \\ - 1 \\ \hline \end{array}$$
$$\begin{array}{r} 31 \\ + 1 \\ \hline \end{array}$$
$$\begin{array}{r} 10 \\ - 5 \\ \hline \end{array}$$

Name _____

Adding two-digit numbers. No regrouping.

A.
$$\begin{array}{r} 61 \\ + 25 \\ \hline \end{array} \qquad \begin{array}{r} 12 \\ + 31 \\ \hline \end{array} \qquad \begin{array}{r} 20 \\ + 47 \\ \hline \end{array} \qquad \begin{array}{r} 24 \\ + 21 \\ \hline \end{array} \qquad \begin{array}{r} 76 \\ + 12 \\ \hline \end{array} \qquad \begin{array}{r} 16 \\ + 61 \\ \hline \end{array}$$

B.
$$\begin{array}{r} 44 \\ + 24 \\ \hline \end{array} \qquad \begin{array}{r} 82 \\ + 16 \\ \hline \end{array} \qquad \begin{array}{r} 46 \\ + 12 \\ \hline \end{array} \qquad \begin{array}{r} 11 \\ + 86 \\ \hline \end{array} \qquad \begin{array}{r} 52 \\ + 14 \\ \hline \end{array} \qquad \begin{array}{r} 19 \\ + 40 \\ \hline \end{array}$$

C.
$$\begin{array}{r} 22 \\ + 12 \\ \hline \end{array} \qquad \begin{array}{r} 15 \\ + 41 \\ \hline \end{array} \qquad \begin{array}{r} 60 \\ + 29 \\ \hline \end{array} \qquad \begin{array}{r} 34 \\ + 12 \\ \hline \end{array} \qquad \begin{array}{r} 81 \\ + 11 \\ \hline \end{array} \qquad \begin{array}{r} 22 \\ + 62 \\ \hline \end{array}$$

Subtracting with two-digit numbers. No regrouping.

D.
$$\begin{array}{r} 42 \\ - 31 \\ \hline \end{array} \qquad \begin{array}{r} 87 \\ - 41 \\ \hline \end{array} \qquad \begin{array}{r} 39 \\ - 21 \\ \hline \end{array} \qquad \begin{array}{r} 93 \\ - 81 \\ \hline \end{array} \qquad \begin{array}{r} 26 \\ - 13 \\ \hline \end{array} \qquad \begin{array}{r} 76 \\ - 61 \\ \hline \end{array}$$

E.
$$\begin{array}{r} 58 \\ - 41 \\ \hline \end{array} \qquad \begin{array}{r} 99 \\ - 18 \\ \hline \end{array} \qquad \begin{array}{r} 65 \\ - 31 \\ \hline \end{array} \qquad \begin{array}{r} 76 \\ - 13 \\ \hline \end{array} \qquad \begin{array}{r} 63 \\ - 52 \\ \hline \end{array} \qquad \begin{array}{r} 47 \\ - 26 \\ \hline \end{array}$$

F.
$$\begin{array}{r} 64 \\ - 11 \\ \hline \end{array} \qquad \begin{array}{r} 56 \\ - 15 \\ \hline \end{array} \qquad \begin{array}{r} 44 \\ - 13 \\ \hline \end{array} \qquad \begin{array}{r} 85 \\ - 14 \\ \hline \end{array} \qquad \begin{array}{r} 58 \\ - 44 \\ \hline \end{array} \qquad \begin{array}{r} 84 \\ - 72 \\ \hline \end{array}$$

Name _____

Addition and subtraction practice. No regrouping.

A.
$$30 + 16$$
$$74 + 14$$
$$38 - 17$$
$$10 - 9$$
$$85 - 11$$
$$86 - 43$$

B.
$$18 - 14$$
$$31 + 13$$
$$22 + 64$$
$$52 + 2$$
$$75 - 14$$
$$11 + 85$$

C.
$$12 + 56$$
$$64 + 10$$
$$8 + 2$$
$$62 - 31$$
$$81 + 12$$
$$36 - 21$$

D.
$$17 - 6$$
$$94 - 82$$
$$23 + 13$$
$$5 + 5$$
$$49 - 28$$
$$83 + 1$$

E.
$$71 + 4$$
$$60 + 20$$
$$28 - 11$$
$$96 - 5$$
$$61 + 7$$
$$10 - 5$$

F.
$$54 + 12$$
$$48 - 17$$
$$9 + 1$$
$$49 - 31$$
$$93 - 12$$
$$94 - 11$$

Name _____

Word Math. Solve the problems.   Show your work.

A. Matt read 26 pages last week and 41 pages this
    week. How many pages did Matt read in all?

Answer: _____
_____

B. Erin drew 39 pictures. She gave 18 of the pictures to
    her friends. How many pictures does she have now?

Answer: _____
_____

C. Mom baked 36 cupcakes. The children ate a total of
    23 cupcakes. How many cupcakes are left?

Answer: _____
_____

D. Lily invited 18 friends to her party. Four friends were
    sick and did not come. How many friends did come
    to her party?

Answer: _____
_____

E. The art room in Abby's school has 24 blue chairs,
    14 green chairs, and 12 round tables. What is the
    total number of chairs?

Answer: _____

Name _____

Adding two- and one-digit numbers. Regrouping to the 10's.

A.
| 27 | 28 | 1
29 | 35 | 14 | 58 |
| + 1 | + 1 | + 1
0 | + 5 | + 4 | + 2 |

B.
| 30 | 72 | 43 | 51 | 85 | 92 |
| + 3 | + 8 | + 3 | + 9 | + 5 | + 6 |

C.
| 15 | 42 | 36 | 82 | 61 | 21 |
| + 5 | + 4 | + 1 | + 0 | + 9 | + 4 |

Addition and subtraction practice. Addition regrouping.

D.
| 73 | 49 | 66 | 22 | 46 | 34 |
| + 3 | + 1 | + 2 | + 8 | − 3 | + 2 |

E.
| 48 | 10 | 65 | 81 | 95 | 10 |
| + 1 | − 5 | + 5 | + 9 | − 4 | + 9 |

F.
| 61 | 18 | 91 | 73 | 90 | 58 |
| + 2 | + 2 | + 1 | − 1 | + 6 | − 7 |

Addition and Subtraction: Beyond Math Facts

Name _____

Addition and subtraction practice. Addition regrouping.

A.	41 + 3	33 − 2	79 + 1	61 + 28	51 + 2	68 − 31
B.	10 − 1	55 + 5	32 + 16	74 + 2	41 + 20	32 + 8
C.	41 + 46	99 − 11	92 + 4	24 + 24	69 − 18	21 + 47
D.	11 + 9	35 + 31	81 + 5	82 − 41	10 − 9	94 − 12
E.	20 + 8	56 + 2	64 − 53	48 − 4	74 − 61	56 + 1
F.	23 + 63	19 + 1	45 + 5	10 − 5	88 + 2	33 + 3

Name _____

Review adding two- and one-digit numbers. Regrouping.

A.
$\begin{array}{r} 26 \\ + 6 \\ \hline \end{array}$
$\begin{array}{r} 68 \\ + 9 \\ \hline \end{array}$
$\begin{array}{r} 32 \\ + 4 \\ \hline \end{array}$
$\begin{array}{r} 53 \\ + 2 \\ \hline \end{array}$
$\begin{array}{r} 87 \\ + 7 \\ \hline \end{array}$
$\begin{array}{r} 39 \\ + 6 \\ \hline \end{array}$

B.
$\begin{array}{r} 84 \\ + 6 \\ \hline \end{array}$
$\begin{array}{r} 93 \\ + 4 \\ \hline \end{array}$
$\begin{array}{r} 25 \\ + 5 \\ \hline \end{array}$
$\begin{array}{r} 71 \\ + 9 \\ \hline \end{array}$
$\begin{array}{r} 29 \\ + 2 \\ \hline \end{array}$
$\begin{array}{r} 14 \\ + 3 \\ \hline \end{array}$

C.
$\begin{array}{r} 49 \\ + 4 \\ \hline \end{array}$
$\begin{array}{r} 79 \\ + 3 \\ \hline \end{array}$
$\begin{array}{r} 15 \\ + 3 \\ \hline \end{array}$
$\begin{array}{r} 17 \\ + 9 \\ \hline \end{array}$
$\begin{array}{r} 48 \\ + 2 \\ \hline \end{array}$
$\begin{array}{r} 22 \\ + 3 \\ \hline \end{array}$

Review addition and subtraction. Addition regrouping.

D.
$\begin{array}{r} 55 \\ + 9 \\ \hline \end{array}$
$\begin{array}{r} 78 \\ - 4 \\ \hline \end{array}$
$\begin{array}{r} 73 \\ + 5 \\ \hline \end{array}$
$\begin{array}{r} 62 \\ + 8 \\ \hline \end{array}$
$\begin{array}{r} 12 \\ - 6 \\ \hline \end{array}$
$\begin{array}{r} 39 \\ + 8 \\ \hline \end{array}$

E.
$\begin{array}{r} 82 \\ + 9 \\ \hline \end{array}$
$\begin{array}{r} 66 \\ + 6 \\ \hline \end{array}$
$\begin{array}{r} 92 \\ - 0 \\ \hline \end{array}$
$\begin{array}{r} 42 \\ + 3 \\ \hline \end{array}$
$\begin{array}{r} 27 \\ + 7 \\ \hline \end{array}$
$\begin{array}{r} 95 \\ + 3 \\ \hline \end{array}$

F.
$\begin{array}{r} 56 \\ - 6 \\ \hline \end{array}$
$\begin{array}{r} 14 \\ - 7 \\ \hline \end{array}$
$\begin{array}{r} 49 \\ + 7 \\ \hline \end{array}$
$\begin{array}{r} 39 \\ + 1 \\ \hline \end{array}$
$\begin{array}{r} 86 \\ + 2 \\ \hline \end{array}$
$\begin{array}{r} 56 \\ + 4 \\ \hline \end{array}$

Name _____

Review addition and subtraction. Addition regrouping.

A.
$$89 + 5 \qquad 24 + 9 \qquad 14 - 7 \qquad 38 - 0 \qquad 19 + 8 \qquad 62 + 3$$

B.
$$98 - 14 \qquad 36 + 9 \qquad 57 - 6 \qquad 72 + 6 \qquad 25 - 5 \qquad 71 - 10$$

C.
$$55 + 3 \qquad 64 + 6 \qquad 23 + 4 \qquad 93 - 83 \qquad 37 + 7 \qquad 68 - 37$$

D.
$$14 - 13 \qquad 36 + 6 \qquad 86 - 5 \qquad 16 + 70 \qquad 31 + 17 \qquad 67 + 9$$

E.
$$63 + 9 \qquad 93 + 2 \qquad 48 - 11 \qquad 16 + 4 \qquad 23 - 2 \qquad 82 + 8$$

F.
$$40 + 35 \qquad 79 + 2 \qquad 83 + 5 \qquad 54 - 42 \qquad 29 + 7 \qquad 49 + 9$$

Name _____

Subtracting with two- and one-digit numbers. Regrouping from the 10's.

A.
$$\begin{array}{r} 79 \\ -\ 8 \\ \hline \end{array}$$
$$\begin{array}{r} 41 \\ -\ 1 \\ \hline \end{array}$$
$$\begin{array}{r} {}^2\cancel{3}{}^1 0 \\ -\ 1 \\ \hline \end{array}$$
$$\begin{array}{r} {}^4\cancel{5}{}^1 2 \\ -\ 6 \\ \hline \end{array}$$
$$\begin{array}{r} 56 \\ -\ 5 \\ \hline \end{array}$$
$$\begin{array}{r} 40 \\ -\ 5 \\ \hline \end{array}$$

B.
$$\begin{array}{r} 20 \\ -\ 9 \\ \hline \end{array}$$
$$\begin{array}{r} 85 \\ -\ 4 \\ \hline \end{array}$$
$$\begin{array}{r} 27 \\ -\ 7 \\ \hline \end{array}$$
$$\begin{array}{r} 64 \\ -\ 7 \\ \hline \end{array}$$
$$\begin{array}{r} 24 \\ -\ 2 \\ \hline \end{array}$$
$$\begin{array}{r} 70 \\ -\ 1 \\ \hline \end{array}$$

C.
$$\begin{array}{r} 62 \\ -\ 0 \\ \hline \end{array}$$
$$\begin{array}{r} 89 \\ -\ 1 \\ \hline \end{array}$$
$$\begin{array}{r} 36 \\ -\ 3 \\ \hline \end{array}$$
$$\begin{array}{r} 28 \\ -\ 4 \\ \hline \end{array}$$
$$\begin{array}{r} 40 \\ -\ 9 \\ \hline \end{array}$$
$$\begin{array}{r} 35 \\ -\ 1 \\ \hline \end{array}$$

Addition and subtraction practice. Regrouping.

D.
$$\begin{array}{r} 49 \\ +\ 6 \\ \hline \end{array}$$
$$\begin{array}{r} 92 \\ -\ 6 \\ \hline \end{array}$$
$$\begin{array}{r} 86 \\ +\ 4 \\ \hline \end{array}$$
$$\begin{array}{r} 90 \\ -\ 5 \\ \hline \end{array}$$
$$\begin{array}{r} 22 \\ -\ 1 \\ \hline \end{array}$$
$$\begin{array}{r} 39 \\ +\ 9 \\ \hline \end{array}$$

E.
$$\begin{array}{r} 73 \\ +\ 2 \\ \hline \end{array}$$
$$\begin{array}{r} 44 \\ -\ 7 \\ \hline \end{array}$$
$$\begin{array}{r} 70 \\ -\ 9 \\ \hline \end{array}$$
$$\begin{array}{r} 62 \\ -\ 6 \\ \hline \end{array}$$
$$\begin{array}{r} 33 \\ -\ 3 \\ \hline \end{array}$$
$$\begin{array}{r} 53 \\ +\ 5 \\ \hline \end{array}$$

F.
$$\begin{array}{r} 60 \\ -\ 1 \\ \hline \end{array}$$
$$\begin{array}{r} 94 \\ +\ 3 \\ \hline \end{array}$$
$$\begin{array}{r} 74 \\ -\ 7 \\ \hline \end{array}$$
$$\begin{array}{r} 14 \\ +\ 6 \\ \hline \end{array}$$
$$\begin{array}{r} 43 \\ -\ 1 \\ \hline \end{array}$$
$$\begin{array}{r} 80 \\ -\ 5 \\ \hline \end{array}$$

Name _____

Addition and subtraction practice. Regrouping.

A.	12 + 8	89 + 6	70 − 5	24 + 6	98 − 7	45 + 5
B.	24 − 7	97 − 1	27 + 9	88 − 7	68 + 2	58 + 0
C.	32 + 9	40 + 7	65 + 3	32 − 6	43 + 9	53 + 4
D.	82 + 3	18 − 8	26 − 0	36 + 2	30 − 9	89 + 1
E.	68 − 4	44 − 2	38 + 9	74 + 2	74 + 9	90 − 1
F.	60 − 9	19 + 5	72 − 6	46 + 4	94 − 7	59 + 4

Name _____

Addition and subtraction practice. Regrouping.

A.
$$\begin{array}{r} 89 \\ +\ 2 \\ \hline \end{array}\qquad \begin{array}{r} 76 \\ +\ 4 \\ \hline \end{array}\qquad \begin{array}{r} 40 \\ -\ 1 \\ \hline \end{array}\qquad \begin{array}{r} 22 \\ -\ 6 \\ \hline \end{array}\qquad \begin{array}{r} 45 \\ +43 \\ \hline \end{array}\qquad \begin{array}{r} 66 \\ -\ 5 \\ \hline \end{array}$$

B.
$$\begin{array}{r} 86 \\ -71 \\ \hline \end{array}\qquad \begin{array}{r} 53 \\ -51 \\ \hline \end{array}\qquad \begin{array}{r} 46 \\ +\ 6 \\ \hline \end{array}\qquad \begin{array}{r} 68 \\ +21 \\ \hline \end{array}\qquad \begin{array}{r} 34 \\ -\ 7 \\ \hline \end{array}\qquad \begin{array}{r} 39 \\ +\ 7 \\ \hline \end{array}$$

C.
$$\begin{array}{r} 59 \\ +\ 9 \\ \hline \end{array}\qquad \begin{array}{r} 13 \\ +52 \\ \hline \end{array}\qquad \begin{array}{r} 96 \\ -\ 3 \\ \hline \end{array}\qquad \begin{array}{r} 22 \\ +\ 6 \\ \hline \end{array}\qquad \begin{array}{r} 52 \\ +\ 3 \\ \hline \end{array}\qquad \begin{array}{r} 21 \\ +\ 9 \\ \hline \end{array}$$

D.
$$\begin{array}{r} 42 \\ -\ 6 \\ \hline \end{array}\qquad \begin{array}{r} 85 \\ +\ 9 \\ \hline \end{array}\qquad \begin{array}{r} 95 \\ -\ 5 \\ \hline \end{array}\qquad \begin{array}{r} 80 \\ -\ 1 \\ \hline \end{array}\qquad \begin{array}{r} 44 \\ +\ 6 \\ \hline \end{array}\qquad \begin{array}{r} 20 \\ +22 \\ \hline \end{array}$$

E.
$$\begin{array}{r} 63 \\ +15 \\ \hline \end{array}\qquad \begin{array}{r} 79 \\ +\ 8 \\ \hline \end{array}\qquad \begin{array}{r} 72 \\ +14 \\ \hline \end{array}\qquad \begin{array}{r} 54 \\ -\ 3 \\ \hline \end{array}\qquad \begin{array}{r} 80 \\ -\ 9 \\ \hline \end{array}\qquad \begin{array}{r} 34 \\ +33 \\ \hline \end{array}$$

F.
$$\begin{array}{r} 56 \\ +\ 9 \\ \hline \end{array}\qquad \begin{array}{r} 20 \\ -\ 5 \\ \hline \end{array}\qquad \begin{array}{r} 39 \\ -20 \\ \hline \end{array}\qquad \begin{array}{r} 19 \\ +\ 3 \\ \hline \end{array}\qquad \begin{array}{r} 81 \\ +\ 6 \\ \hline \end{array}\qquad \begin{array}{r} 54 \\ -\ 7 \\ \hline \end{array}$$

Name _____

Word Math. Solve the problems.   Show your work.

A. Will had $50. He spent $9 at the mall. How much
    money does he have left?

Answer: _____
_____

B. Lizzy saw 6 boys and 34 girls playing tennis.
    How many children did she see altogether?

Answer: _____
_____

C. Jenn and Madison made sugar cookies. It took
    25 minutes to mix the cookie dough and 9
    minutes to bake. How long did it take in all?

Answer: _____
_____

D. Louis likes to play basketball. He scored 7 points
    last week and 44 points this week. How many more
    points did Louis score this week?

Answer: _____
_____

E. Danny had a new book. He read for 34 minutes on
    Monday, 20 minutes on Tuesday, and 53 minutes on
    Friday. How much time in all did he read on Monday
    and Friday?

Answer: _____

Name _____

Adding two-digit numbers. Regrouping to the 100's.

A.	82 + 13	83 + 23	71 + 75	62 + 94	24 + 83	93 + 91
B.	94 + 43	22 + 26	13 + 74	62 + 66	51 + 90	31 + 44
C.	61 + 48	93 + 85	35 + 33	72 + 91	52 + 33	92 + 13

Addition and subtraction practice. Regrouping.

D.	11 + 92	52 − 6	23 + 92	44 + 62	53 − 41	84 − 7
E.	33 + 95	41 + 31	71 + 78	44 − 30	20 − 1	43 − 2
F.	30 − 5	63 − 33	82 + 92	93 − 91	55 + 53	89 − 78

Addition and Subtraction: Beyond Math Facts

Name _____

Addition and subtraction practice. Regrouping.

A.
$$\begin{array}{r} 43 \\ + 65 \\ \hline \end{array}$$
$$\begin{array}{r} 74 \\ - 7 \\ \hline \end{array}$$
$$\begin{array}{r} 41 \\ + 91 \\ \hline \end{array}$$
$$\begin{array}{r} 65 \\ - 14 \\ \hline \end{array}$$
$$\begin{array}{r} 50 \\ - 9 \\ \hline \end{array}$$
$$\begin{array}{r} 46 \\ - 35 \\ \hline \end{array}$$

B.
$$\begin{array}{r} 92 \\ + 92 \\ \hline \end{array}$$
$$\begin{array}{r} 32 \\ + 26 \\ \hline \end{array}$$
$$\begin{array}{r} 84 \\ - 42 \\ \hline \end{array}$$
$$\begin{array}{r} 95 \\ + 61 \\ \hline \end{array}$$
$$\begin{array}{r} 83 \\ + 94 \\ \hline \end{array}$$
$$\begin{array}{r} 77 \\ + 71 \\ \hline \end{array}$$

C.
$$\begin{array}{r} 33 \\ + 42 \\ \hline \end{array}$$
$$\begin{array}{r} 28 \\ - 7 \\ \hline \end{array}$$
$$\begin{array}{r} 60 \\ - 5 \\ \hline \end{array}$$
$$\begin{array}{r} 76 \\ - 73 \\ \hline \end{array}$$
$$\begin{array}{r} 40 \\ + 42 \\ \hline \end{array}$$
$$\begin{array}{r} 64 \\ + 43 \\ \hline \end{array}$$

D.
$$\begin{array}{r} 30 \\ - 1 \\ \hline \end{array}$$
$$\begin{array}{r} 56 \\ + 31 \\ \hline \end{array}$$
$$\begin{array}{r} 27 \\ - 26 \\ \hline \end{array}$$
$$\begin{array}{r} 91 \\ + 13 \\ \hline \end{array}$$
$$\begin{array}{r} 64 \\ - 33 \\ \hline \end{array}$$
$$\begin{array}{r} 94 \\ + 72 \\ \hline \end{array}$$

E.
$$\begin{array}{r} 95 \\ + 23 \\ \hline \end{array}$$
$$\begin{array}{r} 98 \\ - 81 \\ \hline \end{array}$$
$$\begin{array}{r} 80 \\ + 20 \\ \hline \end{array}$$
$$\begin{array}{r} 93 \\ + 53 \\ \hline \end{array}$$
$$\begin{array}{r} 25 \\ + 13 \\ \hline \end{array}$$
$$\begin{array}{r} 64 \\ + 64 \\ \hline \end{array}$$

F.
$$\begin{array}{r} 12 \\ + 93 \\ \hline \end{array}$$
$$\begin{array}{r} 64 \\ + 21 \\ \hline \end{array}$$
$$\begin{array}{r} 84 \\ - 11 \\ \hline \end{array}$$
$$\begin{array}{r} 51 \\ + 56 \\ \hline \end{array}$$
$$\begin{array}{r} 82 \\ - 6 \\ \hline \end{array}$$
$$\begin{array}{r} 95 \\ - 90 \\ \hline \end{array}$$

Name _____

Review addition and subtraction. Regrouping.

A.
$$68 + 8 \qquad 25 + 8 \qquad 59 - 26 \qquad 34 + 5 \qquad 64 - 7 \qquad 23 - 5$$

B.
$$89 - 33 \qquad 51 + 41 \qquad 83 + 56 \qquad 67 - 23 \qquad 46 - 8 \qquad 85 - 23$$

C.
$$78 - 9 \qquad 54 - 34 \qquad 28 - 3 \qquad 65 + 34 \qquad 34 + 6 \qquad 89 + 8$$

D.
$$60 - 2 \qquad 75 - 42 \qquad 83 + 85 \qquad 98 - 35 \qquad 88 - 52 \qquad 46 + 52$$

E.
$$24 + 84 \qquad 90 - 9 \qquad 32 + 63 \qquad 78 - 34 \qquad 96 - 62 \qquad 47 + 9$$

F.
$$77 - 64 \qquad 53 + 85 \qquad 93 - 5 \qquad 23 - 8 \qquad 56 - 8 \qquad 48 + 5$$

Name _____

Review addition and subtraction. Regrouping.

A.
$$89 - 56$$ $$62 + 93$$ $$85 + 54$$ $$94 - 7$$ $$48 + 8$$ $$27 - 3$$

B.
$$33 + 6$$ $$83 - 8$$ $$32 + 8$$ $$60 + 66$$ $$76 - 42$$ $$26 + 4$$

C.
$$56 + 6$$ $$20 - 5$$ $$49 + 3$$ $$25 - 3$$ $$48 - 9$$ $$68 - 52$$

D.
$$86 + 23$$ $$18 + 5$$ $$96 - 8$$ $$65 - 22$$ $$53 + 83$$ $$24 + 95$$

E.
$$33 - 8$$ $$68 - 5$$ $$74 + 75$$ $$76 - 6$$ $$36 + 12$$ $$62 - 6$$

F.
$$78 - 33$$ $$95 - 30$$ $$73 - 5$$ $$72 + 9$$ $$40 - 2$$ $$52 + 94$$

Name _____

Adding three numbers in a column.

A.
$$\begin{array}{r} 2 \\ 2 \\ +2 \\ \hline \end{array} \qquad \begin{array}{r} 3 \\ 3 \\ +2 \\ \hline \end{array} \qquad \begin{array}{r} 4 \\ 2 \\ +1 \\ \hline \end{array} \qquad \begin{array}{r} 1 \\ 1 \\ +8 \\ \hline \end{array} \qquad \begin{array}{r} 4 \\ 2 \\ +2 \\ \hline \end{array} \qquad \begin{array}{r} 1 \\ 6 \\ +6 \\ \hline \end{array}$$

B.
$$\begin{array}{r} 1 \\ 8 \\ +5 \\ \hline \end{array} \qquad \begin{array}{r} 1 \\ 8 \\ +9 \\ \hline \end{array} \qquad \begin{array}{r} 9 \\ 1 \\ +1 \\ \hline \end{array} \qquad \begin{array}{r} 1 \\ 5 \\ +3 \\ \hline \end{array} \qquad \begin{array}{r} 1 \\ 9 \\ +5 \\ \hline \end{array} \qquad \begin{array}{r} 1 \\ 6 \\ +2 \\ \hline \end{array}$$

C.
$$\begin{array}{r} 3 \\ 3 \\ +4 \\ \hline \end{array} \qquad \begin{array}{r} 1 \\ 4 \\ +5 \\ \hline \end{array} \qquad \begin{array}{r} 4 \\ 3 \\ +1 \\ \hline \end{array} \qquad \begin{array}{r} 1 \\ 6 \\ +4 \\ \hline \end{array} \qquad \begin{array}{r} 2 \\ 6 \\ +6 \\ \hline \end{array} \qquad \begin{array}{r} 8 \\ 1 \\ +8 \\ \hline \end{array}$$

D.
$$\begin{array}{r} 1 \\ 8 \\ +2 \\ \hline \end{array} \qquad \begin{array}{r} 1 \\ 9 \\ +9 \\ \hline \end{array} \qquad \begin{array}{r} 9 \\ 1 \\ +7 \\ \hline \end{array} \qquad \begin{array}{r} 1 \\ 3 \\ +6 \\ \hline \end{array} \qquad \begin{array}{r} 5 \\ 3 \\ +2 \\ \hline \end{array} \qquad \begin{array}{r} 1 \\ 4 \\ +9 \\ \hline \end{array}$$

Name _____

Adding two-digit numbers. Regrouping to the 10's or 100's.

A.
$$\begin{array}{r} \scriptstyle 1 \\ 14 \\ +\ 19 \\ \hline 3 \end{array}$$
$$\begin{array}{r} 35 \\ +\ 48 \\ \hline \end{array}$$
$$\begin{array}{r} 55 \\ +\ 93 \\ \hline \end{array}$$
$$\begin{array}{r} 47 \\ +\ 27 \\ \hline \end{array}$$
$$\begin{array}{r} 10 \\ +\ 24 \\ \hline \end{array}$$
$$\begin{array}{r} 82 \\ +\ 82 \\ \hline \end{array}$$

B.
$$\begin{array}{r} 19 \\ +\ 79 \\ \hline \end{array}$$
$$\begin{array}{r} 46 \\ +\ 13 \\ \hline \end{array}$$
$$\begin{array}{r} 29 \\ +\ 65 \\ \hline \end{array}$$
$$\begin{array}{r} 75 \\ +\ 15 \\ \hline \end{array}$$
$$\begin{array}{r} 76 \\ +\ 92 \\ \hline \end{array}$$
$$\begin{array}{r} 52 \\ +\ 18 \\ \hline \end{array}$$

C.
$$\begin{array}{r} 45 \\ +\ 54 \\ \hline \end{array}$$
$$\begin{array}{r} 39 \\ +\ 26 \\ \hline \end{array}$$
$$\begin{array}{r} 40 \\ +\ 65 \\ \hline \end{array}$$
$$\begin{array}{r} 18 \\ +\ 45 \\ \hline \end{array}$$
$$\begin{array}{r} 84 \\ +\ 25 \\ \hline \end{array}$$
$$\begin{array}{r} 49 \\ +\ 37 \\ \hline \end{array}$$

Addition and subtraction practice. Addition regrouping.

D.
$$\begin{array}{r} 31 \\ +\ 59 \\ \hline \end{array}$$
$$\begin{array}{r} 52 \\ +\ 46 \\ \hline \end{array}$$
$$\begin{array}{r} 28 \\ +\ 12 \\ \hline \end{array}$$
$$\begin{array}{r} 63 \\ +\ 64 \\ \hline \end{array}$$
$$\begin{array}{r} 30 \\ +\ 60 \\ \hline \end{array}$$
$$\begin{array}{r} 58 \\ -\ 25 \\ \hline \end{array}$$

E.
$$\begin{array}{r} 39 \\ +\ 32 \\ \hline \end{array}$$
$$\begin{array}{r} 38 \\ -\ 28 \\ \hline \end{array}$$
$$\begin{array}{r} 56 \\ +\ 83 \\ \hline \end{array}$$
$$\begin{array}{r} 95 \\ -\ 63 \\ \hline \end{array}$$
$$\begin{array}{r} 87 \\ -\ 34 \\ \hline \end{array}$$
$$\begin{array}{r} 68 \\ +\ 28 \\ \hline \end{array}$$

F.
$$\begin{array}{r} 87 \\ -\ 23 \\ \hline \end{array}$$
$$\begin{array}{r} 53 \\ +\ 39 \\ \hline \end{array}$$
$$\begin{array}{r} 80 \\ +\ 55 \\ \hline \end{array}$$
$$\begin{array}{r} 29 \\ +\ 31 \\ \hline \end{array}$$
$$\begin{array}{r} 84 \\ +\ 93 \\ \hline \end{array}$$
$$\begin{array}{r} 69 \\ -\ 23 \\ \hline \end{array}$$

Name _____

Addition and subtraction practice. Regrouping.

A.	$\begin{array}{r} 35 \\ + 39 \\ \hline \end{array}$	$\begin{array}{r} 96 \\ + 42 \\ \hline \end{array}$	$\begin{array}{r} 74 \\ - 32 \\ \hline \end{array}$	$\begin{array}{r} 93 \\ + 16 \\ \hline \end{array}$	$\begin{array}{r} 66 \\ - 8 \\ \hline \end{array}$	$\begin{array}{r} 86 \\ - 21 \\ \hline \end{array}$

A.
$$\begin{array}{r} 35 \\ + 39 \\ \hline \end{array} \quad \begin{array}{r} 96 \\ + 42 \\ \hline \end{array} \quad \begin{array}{r} 74 \\ - 32 \\ \hline \end{array} \quad \begin{array}{r} 93 \\ + 16 \\ \hline \end{array} \quad \begin{array}{r} 66 \\ - 8 \\ \hline \end{array} \quad \begin{array}{r} 86 \\ - 21 \\ \hline \end{array}$$

B.
$$\begin{array}{r} 78 \\ - 42 \\ \hline \end{array} \quad \begin{array}{r} 12 \\ + 82 \\ \hline \end{array} \quad \begin{array}{r} 99 \\ - 36 \\ \hline \end{array} \quad \begin{array}{r} 64 \\ + 65 \\ \hline \end{array} \quad \begin{array}{r} 58 \\ - 37 \\ \hline \end{array} \quad \begin{array}{r} 36 \\ + 46 \\ \hline \end{array}$$

C.
$$\begin{array}{r} 60 \\ - 9 \\ \hline \end{array} \quad \begin{array}{r} 56 \\ - 53 \\ \hline \end{array} \quad \begin{array}{r} 26 \\ + 69 \\ \hline \end{array} \quad \begin{array}{r} 50 \\ - 20 \\ \hline \end{array} \quad \begin{array}{r} 75 \\ + 74 \\ \hline \end{array} \quad \begin{array}{r} 53 \\ - 5 \\ \hline \end{array}$$

D.
$$\begin{array}{r} 96 \\ + 63 \\ \hline \end{array} \quad \begin{array}{r} 82 \\ - 32 \\ \hline \end{array} \quad \begin{array}{r} 38 \\ - 9 \\ \hline \end{array} \quad \begin{array}{r} 86 \\ - 52 \\ \hline \end{array} \quad \begin{array}{r} 56 \\ + 34 \\ \hline \end{array} \quad \begin{array}{r} 99 \\ - 68 \\ \hline \end{array}$$

E.
$$\begin{array}{r} 42 \\ + 49 \\ \hline \end{array} \quad \begin{array}{r} 82 \\ + 23 \\ \hline \end{array} \quad \begin{array}{r} 67 \\ - 4 \\ \hline \end{array} \quad \begin{array}{r} 38 \\ + 18 \\ \hline \end{array} \quad \begin{array}{r} 44 \\ - 7 \\ \hline \end{array} \quad \begin{array}{r} 90 \\ - 1 \\ \hline \end{array}$$

F.
$$\begin{array}{r} 19 \\ + 63 \\ \hline \end{array} \quad \begin{array}{r} 73 \\ - 8 \\ \hline \end{array} \quad \begin{array}{r} 45 \\ + 38 \\ \hline \end{array} \quad \begin{array}{r} 90 \\ - 2 \\ \hline \end{array} \quad \begin{array}{r} 84 \\ + 52 \\ \hline \end{array} \quad \begin{array}{r} 22 \\ - 6 \\ \hline \end{array}$$

Addition and Subtraction: Beyond Math Facts

Name _____

Addition and subtraction practice. Regrouping.

A.	$\begin{array}{r} 43 \\ -\ 8 \\ \hline \end{array}$	$\begin{array}{r} 53 \\ +46 \\ \hline \end{array}$	$\begin{array}{r} 83 \\ +82 \\ \hline \end{array}$	$\begin{array}{r} 18 \\ +35 \\ \hline \end{array}$	$\begin{array}{r} 97 \\ -64 \\ \hline \end{array}$	$\begin{array}{r} 74 \\ +\ 6 \\ \hline \end{array}$

A.   43   53   83   18   97   74
    − 8 + 46 + 82 + 35 − 64 + 6

B.   88   20   28   65   59   94
    − 34 − 2 + 29 + 18 − 3 + 93

C.   93   29   62   76   40   48
    + 73 + 41 + 36 − 8 − 9 − 32

D.   37   48   36   50   28   79
    + 49 − 45 + 24 − 5 + 35 + 10

E.   54   56   80   15   73   63
    + 55 − 42 − 2 + 18 + 6 − 5

F.   34   91   28   88   65   57
    + 64 + 57 + 68 − 9 − 23 + 37

Name _____

Subtracting with two-digit numbers. Regrouping.

A.
$$\begin{array}{r} 92 \\ -\ 80 \\ \hline \end{array}$$
$$\begin{array}{r} {}^{4}\!\!\!\not5{}^{1}0 \\ -\ 15 \\ \hline \end{array}$$
$$\begin{array}{r} 70 \\ -\ 19 \\ \hline \end{array}$$
$$\begin{array}{r} 83 \\ -\ 15 \\ \hline \end{array}$$
$$\begin{array}{r} 67 \\ -\ 36 \\ \hline \end{array}$$
$$\begin{array}{r} 68 \\ -\ 59 \\ \hline \end{array}$$

B.
$$\begin{array}{r} 82 \\ -\ 36 \\ \hline \end{array}$$
$$\begin{array}{r} 24 \\ -\ 17 \\ \hline \end{array}$$
$$\begin{array}{r} 69 \\ -\ 26 \\ \hline \end{array}$$
$$\begin{array}{r} 90 \\ -\ 22 \\ \hline \end{array}$$
$$\begin{array}{r} 85 \\ -\ 52 \\ \hline \end{array}$$
$$\begin{array}{r} 63 \\ -\ 18 \\ \hline \end{array}$$

C.
$$\begin{array}{r} 56 \\ -\ 38 \\ \hline \end{array}$$
$$\begin{array}{r} 98 \\ -\ 13 \\ \hline \end{array}$$
$$\begin{array}{r} 38 \\ -\ 12 \\ \hline \end{array}$$
$$\begin{array}{r} 30 \\ -\ 19 \\ \hline \end{array}$$
$$\begin{array}{r} 96 \\ -\ 32 \\ \hline \end{array}$$
$$\begin{array}{r} 87 \\ -\ 40 \\ \hline \end{array}$$

Addition and subtraction practice. Regrouping.

D.
$$\begin{array}{r} 98 \\ -\ 61 \\ \hline \end{array}$$
$$\begin{array}{r} 56 \\ +\ 93 \\ \hline \end{array}$$
$$\begin{array}{r} 39 \\ -\ 23 \\ \hline \end{array}$$
$$\begin{array}{r} 94 \\ +\ 94 \\ \hline \end{array}$$
$$\begin{array}{r} 27 \\ -\ 13 \\ \hline \end{array}$$
$$\begin{array}{r} 95 \\ +\ 34 \\ \hline \end{array}$$

E.
$$\begin{array}{r} 38 \\ +\ 15 \\ \hline \end{array}$$
$$\begin{array}{r} 78 \\ -\ 59 \\ \hline \end{array}$$
$$\begin{array}{r} 83 \\ -\ 48 \\ \hline \end{array}$$
$$\begin{array}{r} 36 \\ +\ 29 \\ \hline \end{array}$$
$$\begin{array}{r} 66 \\ +\ 24 \\ \hline \end{array}$$
$$\begin{array}{r} 53 \\ +\ 85 \\ \hline \end{array}$$

F.
$$\begin{array}{r} 50 \\ -\ 41 \\ \hline \end{array}$$
$$\begin{array}{r} 48 \\ +\ 28 \\ \hline \end{array}$$
$$\begin{array}{r} 51 \\ +\ 58 \\ \hline \end{array}$$
$$\begin{array}{r} 64 \\ -\ 27 \\ \hline \end{array}$$
$$\begin{array}{r} 14 \\ +\ 93 \\ \hline \end{array}$$
$$\begin{array}{r} 75 \\ -\ 13 \\ \hline \end{array}$$

Name _____

Addition and subtraction practice. Regrouping.

A.
$$
\begin{array}{r} 58 \\ + 39 \\ \hline \end{array}
\qquad
\begin{array}{r} 80 \\ - 11 \\ \hline \end{array}
\qquad
\begin{array}{r} 48 \\ + 38 \\ \hline \end{array}
\qquad
\begin{array}{r} 25 \\ + 81 \\ \hline \end{array}
\qquad
\begin{array}{r} 94 \\ - 37 \\ \hline \end{array}
\qquad
\begin{array}{r} 33 \\ - 25 \\ \hline \end{array}
$$

B.
$$
\begin{array}{r} 68 \\ - 32 \\ \hline \end{array}
\qquad
\begin{array}{r} 69 \\ + 26 \\ \hline \end{array}
\qquad
\begin{array}{r} 22 \\ + 18 \\ \hline \end{array}
\qquad
\begin{array}{r} 80 \\ - 69 \\ \hline \end{array}
\qquad
\begin{array}{r} 64 \\ + 95 \\ \hline \end{array}
\qquad
\begin{array}{r} 19 \\ - 16 \\ \hline \end{array}
$$

C.
$$
\begin{array}{r} 42 \\ - 26 \\ \hline \end{array}
\qquad
\begin{array}{r} 84 \\ + 54 \\ \hline \end{array}
\qquad
\begin{array}{r} 48 \\ - 23 \\ \hline \end{array}
\qquad
\begin{array}{r} 35 \\ + 25 \\ \hline \end{array}
\qquad
\begin{array}{r} 83 \\ - 68 \\ \hline \end{array}
\qquad
\begin{array}{r} 73 \\ + 75 \\ \hline \end{array}
$$

D.
$$
\begin{array}{r} 50 \\ + 44 \\ \hline \end{array}
\qquad
\begin{array}{r} 67 \\ - 24 \\ \hline \end{array}
\qquad
\begin{array}{r} 25 \\ + 28 \\ \hline \end{array}
\qquad
\begin{array}{r} 40 \\ - 32 \\ \hline \end{array}
\qquad
\begin{array}{r} 99 \\ + 80 \\ \hline \end{array}
\qquad
\begin{array}{r} 36 \\ + 43 \\ \hline \end{array}
$$

E.
$$
\begin{array}{r} 70 \\ - 12 \\ \hline \end{array}
\qquad
\begin{array}{r} 26 \\ + 66 \\ \hline \end{array}
\qquad
\begin{array}{r} 89 \\ - 83 \\ \hline \end{array}
\qquad
\begin{array}{r} 96 \\ + 93 \\ \hline \end{array}
\qquad
\begin{array}{r} 98 \\ - 29 \\ \hline \end{array}
\qquad
\begin{array}{r} 48 \\ + 42 \\ \hline \end{array}
$$

F.
$$
\begin{array}{r} 72 \\ + 94 \\ \hline \end{array}
\qquad
\begin{array}{r} 53 \\ - 18 \\ \hline \end{array}
\qquad
\begin{array}{r} 67 \\ + 91 \\ \hline \end{array}
\qquad
\begin{array}{r} 49 \\ + 44 \\ \hline \end{array}
\qquad
\begin{array}{r} 52 \\ - 20 \\ \hline \end{array}
\qquad
\begin{array}{r} 40 \\ - 15 \\ \hline \end{array}
$$

Name _____

Adding two-digit numbers. Two-place regrouping.

A.
$$\begin{array}{r} \overset{1}{6}4 \\ +\,19 \\ \hline 3 \end{array} \qquad \begin{array}{r} \overset{1}{1}2 \\ +\,99 \\ \hline 1 \end{array} \qquad \begin{array}{r} 82 \\ +\,58 \\ \hline \end{array} \qquad \begin{array}{r} 95 \\ +\,69 \\ \hline \end{array} \qquad \begin{array}{r} 16 \\ +\,54 \\ \hline \end{array} \qquad \begin{array}{r} 80 \\ +\,93 \\ \hline \end{array}$$

B.
$$\begin{array}{r} 29 \\ +\,61 \\ \hline \end{array} \qquad \begin{array}{r} 54 \\ +\,83 \\ \hline \end{array} \qquad \begin{array}{r} 99 \\ +\,97 \\ \hline \end{array} \qquad \begin{array}{r} 79 \\ +\,92 \\ \hline \end{array} \qquad \begin{array}{r} 71 \\ +\,71 \\ \hline \end{array} \qquad \begin{array}{r} 88 \\ +\,28 \\ \hline \end{array}$$

C.
$$\begin{array}{r} 63 \\ +\,66 \\ \hline \end{array} \qquad \begin{array}{r} 25 \\ +\,35 \\ \hline \end{array} \qquad \begin{array}{r} 48 \\ +\,62 \\ \hline \end{array} \qquad \begin{array}{r} 96 \\ +\,59 \\ \hline \end{array} \qquad \begin{array}{r} 65 \\ +\,34 \\ \hline \end{array} \qquad \begin{array}{r} 23 \\ +\,84 \\ \hline \end{array}$$

Addition and subtraction practice. Regrouping.

D.
$$\begin{array}{r} 65 \\ +\,48 \\ \hline \end{array} \qquad \begin{array}{r} 87 \\ +\,87 \\ \hline \end{array} \qquad \begin{array}{r} 53 \\ -\,25 \\ \hline \end{array} \qquad \begin{array}{r} 98 \\ -\,62 \\ \hline \end{array} \qquad \begin{array}{r} 26 \\ +\,29 \\ \hline \end{array} \qquad \begin{array}{r} 76 \\ -\,58 \\ \hline \end{array}$$

E.
$$\begin{array}{r} 39 \\ +\,98 \\ \hline \end{array} \qquad \begin{array}{r} 54 \\ -\,27 \\ \hline \end{array} \qquad \begin{array}{r} 37 \\ -\,24 \\ \hline \end{array} \qquad \begin{array}{r} 60 \\ -\,22 \\ \hline \end{array} \qquad \begin{array}{r} 46 \\ +\,53 \\ \hline \end{array} \qquad \begin{array}{r} 72 \\ -\,66 \\ \hline \end{array}$$

F.
$$\begin{array}{r} 89 \\ -\,36 \\ \hline \end{array} \qquad \begin{array}{r} 88 \\ -\,25 \\ \hline \end{array} \qquad \begin{array}{r} 93 \\ -\,48 \\ \hline \end{array} \qquad \begin{array}{r} 91 \\ +\,88 \\ \hline \end{array} \qquad \begin{array}{r} 86 \\ -\,65 \\ \hline \end{array} \qquad \begin{array}{r} 26 \\ -\,12 \\ \hline \end{array}$$

Addition and Subtraction: Beyond Math Facts

Name _____

Word Math. Solve the problems.   Show your work.

A.   The Adam City Zoo has a picnic area with 48 large
     tables and 58 smaller tables. Ten schools visit the
     zoo every day. What is the total number of tables at
     the zoo?

Answer: _____
_____

B.   Jordan's father teaches two music classes. There
     are 28 students in the morning class and 33 in the
     afternoon class. How many more students are in the
     afternoon class?

Answer: _____
_____

C.   ESTIMATE this answer:
     There are 79 children at camp on Mondays and
     52 children at camp on Tuesdays. About how many
     children attend camp on Monday and Tuesday?

Answer: _____
_____

D.   Rae received $40 for her birthday. She spent $29 in
     the bookstore and $4 at the ice-cream store. How
     much money did she spend?

Answer: _____
_____

E.   Jennie rode her bike 28 miles this month and
     76 miles last month. Jennie's friend, Stacey, rides
     her bike 60 miles every month. How many more
     miles did Jennie ride last month than this month?

Answer: _____

Name _____

Review adding two-digit numbers. Two-place regrouping.

A.
```
   34        55        16        73        77        35
 + 27      + 45      + 28      + 56      + 14      + 98
```

B.
```
   64        74        86        57        67        64
 + 93      + 44      + 54      + 35      + 87      + 37
```

C.
```
   35        89        44        83        43        58
 + 47      + 19      + 25      + 63      + 70      + 16
```

Review subtraction. Regrouping.

D.
```
   28        87        64        21        69        96
 - 19      - 79      - 45      - 14      - 16      - 47
```

E.
```
   33        72        31        65        84        99
 - 18      - 39      - 27      - 19      - 49      - 95
```

F.
```
   77        98        41        90        43        61
 - 28      - 42      - 12      - 52      - 24      - 29
```

Addition and Subtraction: Beyond Math Facts   **27**

Name _____

Review addition and subtraction. Regrouping.

A.	86 + 63	72 − 33	69 − 24	53 − 49	72 + 48	41 − 17
B.	25 + 47	44 − 25	94 − 19	39 + 68	67 − 58	54 + 87
C.	81 − 44	69 + 35	37 + 55	98 − 53	66 − 39	63 + 84
D.	96 − 45	18 + 96	87 + 84	56 − 37	96 + 28	77 + 59
E.	73 − 15	93 − 24	51 + 74	91 − 59	98 − 30	25 + 24
F.	68 + 25	21 − 17	98 − 82	35 − 26	44 + 76	51 − 24

Name _____

Adding and subtracting with three- and two-digit numbers. Regrouping between 10's and 1's.

A.
```
  134        499        319        406        343
+  17      −  15      +  23      +  18      −  18
```

B.
```
  965        726        838        690        265
−  49      +  36      +  49      −  72      −  56
```

C.
```
  592        170        261        725        256
−  39      −  39      −  24      +  67      +  41
```

D.
```
  627        545        290        981        638
+  34      +  48      −  45      −  42      +  56
```

E.
```
  398        786        139        331        487
−  45      −  18      +  24      +  65      −  49
```

F.
```
  646        537        882        891        949
+  14      +  35      −  66      −  87      +  11
```

Addition and Subtraction: Beyond Math Facts   **29**

Name _____

Adding three- and two-digit numbers. Regrouping to the 10's or 100's.

A.
$$354 + 55 \qquad 766 + 82 \qquad 648 + 35 \qquad 485 + 83 \qquad 864 + 30$$

B.
$$272 + 46 \qquad 449 + 27 \qquad 353 + 72 \qquad 652 + 92 \qquad 976 + 16$$

C.
$$808 + 76 \qquad 216 + 19 \qquad 543 + 44 \qquad 595 + 94 \qquad 873 + 76$$

Subtracting with three- and two-digit numbers. Regrouping from the 100's or 10's.

D.
$$\overset{3}{4}^{1}16 - 73 \qquad 505 - 54 \qquad 686 - 49 \qquad 294 - 75 \qquad 889 - 35$$

E.
$$949 - 76 \qquad 189 - 23 \qquad 753 - 25 \qquad 177 - 83 \qquad 787 - 90$$

F.
$$289 - 74 \qquad 325 - 63 \qquad 632 - 13 \qquad 305 - 12 \qquad 932 - 92$$

Name _____

Addition and subtraction practice. One-place regrouping.

A.
$$260 + 44$$
$$461 - 17$$
$$964 + 19$$
$$749 - 53$$
$$998 - 54$$

B.
$$835 - 29$$
$$183 + 66$$
$$566 - 93$$
$$393 - 28$$
$$764 + 85$$

C.
$$663 - 34$$
$$817 - 94$$
$$183 + 15$$
$$625 + 68$$
$$819 - 28$$

D.
$$735 + 47$$
$$407 - 23$$
$$127 - 19$$
$$425 - 32$$
$$227 + 37$$

E.
$$480 - 69$$
$$954 + 37$$
$$395 - 45$$
$$293 + 83$$
$$518 - 45$$

F.
$$271 + 43$$
$$347 + 45$$
$$726 - 18$$
$$636 + 92$$
$$596 - 37$$

Name _____

Adding and subtracting with money to the dollar place. One-place regrouping.

A.
$7.64
+ .61

$1.44
+ .74

$8.61
− .44

$3.38
− .22

$4.46
+ .38

B.
$2.59
− .64

$2.07
− .26

$9.09
+ .85

$6.52
+ .73

$4.28
− .93

C.
$5.27
+ .49

$3.37
+ .54

$2.36
− .51

$3.59
− .21

$6.49
− .96

Addition and subtraction practice, including money. One-place regrouping.

D.
$8.78
− .59

428
+ 26

746
− 72

$5.85
+ .53

883
+ 22

E.
395
+ 34

$1.38
− .97

414
− 22

$8.71
+ .51

677
− 28

F.
213
+ 86

$5.05
− .93

796
+ 13

919
− 75

$5.14
+ .66

Addition and Subtraction: Beyond Math Facts

Name _____

Adding three- and two-digit numbers. Two-place regrouping.

A.
$\begin{array}{r} 244 \\ +\ 94 \\ \hline \end{array}$
$\begin{array}{r} {\scriptstyle 1\ 1} \\ 355 \\ +\ 57 \\ \hline 12 \end{array}$
$\begin{array}{r} 357 \\ +\ 49 \\ \hline \end{array}$
$\begin{array}{r} 426 \\ +\ 34 \\ \hline \end{array}$
$\begin{array}{r} 775 \\ +\ 79 \\ \hline \end{array}$

B.
$\begin{array}{r} 363 \\ +\ 81 \\ \hline \end{array}$
$\begin{array}{r} 128 \\ +\ 95 \\ \hline \end{array}$
$\begin{array}{r} 334 \\ +\ 47 \\ \hline \end{array}$
$\begin{array}{r} 836 \\ +\ 66 \\ \hline \end{array}$
$\begin{array}{r} 567 \\ +\ 67 \\ \hline \end{array}$

C.
$\begin{array}{r} 287 \\ +\ 95 \\ \hline \end{array}$
$\begin{array}{r} 847 \\ +\ 51 \\ \hline \end{array}$
$\begin{array}{r} 491 \\ +\ 69 \\ \hline \end{array}$
$\begin{array}{r} 294 \\ +\ 77 \\ \hline \end{array}$
$\begin{array}{r} 571 \\ +\ 42 \\ \hline \end{array}$

Addition and subtraction practice. Regrouping.

D.
$\begin{array}{r} 736 \\ -\ 82 \\ \hline \end{array}$
$\begin{array}{r} 391 \\ -\ 47 \\ \hline \end{array}$
$\begin{array}{r} 548 \\ +\ 46 \\ \hline \end{array}$
$\begin{array}{r} 565 \\ +\ 98 \\ \hline \end{array}$
$\begin{array}{r} 972 \\ -\ 39 \\ \hline \end{array}$

E.
$\begin{array}{r} 669 \\ -\ 94 \\ \hline \end{array}$
$\begin{array}{r} 285 \\ +\ 23 \\ \hline \end{array}$
$\begin{array}{r} 615 \\ -\ 42 \\ \hline \end{array}$
$\begin{array}{r} 489 \\ +\ 63 \\ \hline \end{array}$
$\begin{array}{r} 774 \\ -\ 90 \\ \hline \end{array}$

F.
$\begin{array}{r} 259 \\ +\ 78 \\ \hline \end{array}$
$\begin{array}{r} 169 \\ +\ 81 \\ \hline \end{array}$
$\begin{array}{r} 560 \\ +\ 32 \\ \hline \end{array}$
$\begin{array}{r} 932 \\ -\ 16 \\ \hline \end{array}$
$\begin{array}{r} 993 \\ -\ 79 \\ \hline \end{array}$

Addition and Subtraction: Beyond Math Facts

Name _____

Addition and subtraction practice. Regrouping.

A.
$$267 - 83$$ $$572 + 42$$ $$581 - 49$$ $$118 + 26$$ $$799 - 64$$

B.
$$478 + 52$$ $$944 - 92$$ $$283 + 85$$ $$395 + 58$$ $$249 - 93$$

C.
$$660 - 52$$ $$339 + 36$$ $$954 + 12$$ $$612 - 70$$ $$151 - 42$$

D.
$$492 + 46$$ $$846 + 62$$ $$558 - 95$$ $$438 - 42$$ $$159 + 49$$

E.
$$746 - 17$$ $$449 + 72$$ $$881 - 14$$ $$215 + 77$$ $$690 - 15$$

F.
$$877 - 38$$ $$393 + 19$$ $$956 - 62$$ $$789 - 95$$ $$626 + 88$$

Name _____

Word Math. Solve the problems.   Show your work.

A. If 293 children buy lunch at 11 a.m. and 84 children
    buy lunch at noon, how many more children bought
    lunch at 11 a.m.?

Answer: _____
_____

B. Last week, David earned $5.47. This week, his dad
    gave him 75 cents to take out the trash. How much
    money does David have altogether?

Answer: _____
_____

C. ESTIMATE this answer:
    Alex's family went on a family trip. They traveled 86
    miles on the first day, 292 miles the next day, and
    202 miles the last day. About how many more miles
    did they drive on the second day than the first day?

Answer: _____
_____

D. Sarah is 135 centimeters tall. She used a meter stick
    to measure the height of a rosebush growing in her
    garden. It was 55 cm tall when she planted it, and now
    it is 109 cm tall. How much did the rosebush grow?

Answer: _____
_____

E. Jake has collected 226 miniature cars. He saved his
    money and bought 18 more cars. His friend, Eli, has
    72 cars. How many cars do the boys have in all?

Answer: _____

Name _____

Review addition and subtraction. Regrouping.

A.
```
   838        472        985        275        190
 +  24      +  87      –  29      +  36      –  68
```

B.
```
   897        386        570        926        728
 –  25      +  45      –  47      +  58      –  83
```

C.
```
   764        529        178        436        881
 +  73      –  37      +  27      –  84      –  57
```

D.
```
   147        397        152        682        290
 +  73      +  82      –  38      +  78      –  73
```

E.
```
   657        892        447        207        575
 +  65      –  24      +  86      –  82      +  42
```

F.
```
   509        925        708        213        687
 –  32      +  47      –  76      +  87      +  65
```

Name _____

Subtracting with three- and two-digit numbers. Two-place regrouping.

A.
$$
\begin{array}{r} 958 \\ -\ 19 \\ \hline \end{array}
\qquad
\begin{array}{r} 326 \\ -\ 43 \\ \hline \end{array}
\qquad
\begin{array}{r} {}^{5\,12}6\cancel{3}\cancel{4}^{1} \\ -\ 67 \\ \hline 7 \end{array}
\qquad
\begin{array}{r} 470 \\ -\ 78 \\ \hline \end{array}
\qquad
\begin{array}{r} 633 \\ -\ 94 \\ \hline \end{array}
$$

B.
$$
\begin{array}{r} 907 \\ -\ 37 \\ \hline \end{array}
\qquad
\begin{array}{r} 921 \\ -\ 74 \\ \hline \end{array}
\qquad
\begin{array}{r} 716 \\ -\ 59 \\ \hline \end{array}
\qquad
\begin{array}{r} 979 \\ -\ 52 \\ \hline \end{array}
\qquad
\begin{array}{r} 466 \\ -\ 58 \\ \hline \end{array}
$$

C.
$$
\begin{array}{r} 883 \\ -\ 45 \\ \hline \end{array}
\qquad
\begin{array}{r} 203 \\ -\ 90 \\ \hline \end{array}
\qquad
\begin{array}{r} 774 \\ -\ 83 \\ \hline \end{array}
\qquad
\begin{array}{r} 822 \\ -\ 23 \\ \hline \end{array}
\qquad
\begin{array}{r} 539 \\ -\ 97 \\ \hline \end{array}
$$

Addition and subtraction practice. Regrouping.

D.
$$
\begin{array}{r} 707 \\ -\ 82 \\ \hline \end{array}
\qquad
\begin{array}{r} 375 \\ -\ 66 \\ \hline \end{array}
\qquad
\begin{array}{r} 329 \\ -\ 86 \\ \hline \end{array}
\qquad
\begin{array}{r} 142 \\ +\ 85 \\ \hline \end{array}
\qquad
\begin{array}{r} 970 \\ -\ 12 \\ \hline \end{array}
$$

E.
$$
\begin{array}{r} 812 \\ -\ 38 \\ \hline \end{array}
\qquad
\begin{array}{r} 287 \\ +\ 68 \\ \hline \end{array}
\qquad
\begin{array}{r} 564 \\ +\ 59 \\ \hline \end{array}
\qquad
\begin{array}{r} 514 \\ -\ 15 \\ \hline \end{array}
\qquad
\begin{array}{r} 457 \\ +\ 83 \\ \hline \end{array}
$$

F.
$$
\begin{array}{r} 234 \\ +\ 76 \\ \hline \end{array}
\qquad
\begin{array}{r} 168 \\ +\ 24 \\ \hline \end{array}
\qquad
\begin{array}{r} 970 \\ -\ 47 \\ \hline \end{array}
\qquad
\begin{array}{r} 696 \\ +\ 27 \\ \hline \end{array}
\qquad
\begin{array}{r} 325 \\ +\ 76 \\ \hline \end{array}
$$

Addition and Subtraction: Beyond Math Facts **37**

Name _____

Addition and subtraction practice. Regrouping.

A.	128 − 46	532 − 86	970 − 23	252 + 67	880 − 95
B.	465 + 47	784 − 25	383 − 98	319 − 24	677 + 74
C.	883 + 40	169 + 77	223 − 49	729 − 95	405 − 73

Addition and subtraction practice, including money. Two-place regrouping.

D.	$5.66 + .85	$8.61 − .67	309 − 83	743 + 57	$2.84 + .78
E.	950 − 92	$4.44 − .57	$1.59 + .21	$2.53 − .24	666 − 80
F.	$3.86 − .37	872 + 39	989 − 62	$6.17 − .72	$5.77 + .26

Addition and Subtraction: Beyond Math Facts

Name _____

Adding and subtracting with three-digit numbers. One-place regrouping.

A.
$$909 - 286$$
$$214 + 758$$
$$699 - 448$$
$$370 + 240$$
$$692 - 338$$

B.
$$415 + 546$$
$$576 - 218$$
$$453 + 124$$
$$927 - 635$$
$$285 + 573$$

C.
$$370 - 107$$
$$231 + 271$$
$$580 - 422$$
$$919 - 447$$
$$807 - 132$$

D.
$$452 + 395$$
$$182 + 767$$
$$336 - 253$$
$$283 + 643$$
$$727 + 233$$

E.
$$987 - 558$$
$$547 + 248$$
$$826 - 545$$
$$106 + 277$$
$$971 - 742$$

F.
$$373 + 566$$
$$225 + 418$$
$$788 - 592$$
$$694 - 222$$
$$677 + 292$$

Name _____

Adding three-digit numbers. Two-place regrouping.

248	475	676	270	247
+ 124	+ 454	+ 239	+ 383	+ 566

A.

298	636	349	352	541
+ 286	+ 355	+ 282	+ 188	+ 377

B.

363	559	692	269	748
+ 487	+ 264	+ 167	+ 679	+ 237

C.

Subtracting with three-digit numbers. Two-place regrouping.

990	509	352	873	469
− 373	− 491	− 154	− 295	− 344

D.

430	710	597	719	965
− 181	− 308	− 355	− 472	− 229

E.

723	814	617	736	909
− 294	− 687	− 138	− 147	− 177

F.

Name _____

Addition and subtraction practice. Regrouping.

819	187	980	329	630
A. − 743	+ 358	− 543	+ 647	− 185

748	283	569	890	315
B. − 373	+ 167	− 492	− 528	+ 396

174	333	128	457	982
C. + 567	− 248	+ 254	+ 253	− 794

Addition and subtraction practice, including money. Two-place regrouping.

$8.07	$7.18	169	456	$5.07
D. − 6.76	− 5.26	+ 158	+ 524	− 2.95

647	283	$6.41	$5.29	772
E. + 282	+ 374	− 1.97	− 1.97	− 218

$4.39	$9.50	386	287	$8.14
F. + 1.76	− 1.31	+ 587	+ 524	− 5.89

Name _____

Word Math. Solve the problems.   Show your work.

A. Tommy, the male lion, weighs 430 pounds. Dev,
    the female lion, weighs 388 pounds. What is the
    difference in their weights?

Answer: _____

B. On Thursday, Michael had $9.06. He spent $3.47 for
    a large drink and $5.27 for pizza. How much money
    does he have left?

Answer: _____

C. ESTIMATE this answer:
    Lisa had $15.00. If she spent $4.98 for a snack
    and $7.36 for lunch, about how much more did
    she spend for lunch?

Answer: _____

D. Charlotte works in a candy factory. She packed
    447 candy bars today and 486 candy bars
    yesterday. She hopes to pack more than
    500 tomorrow. How many candy bars did
    she pack so far?

Answer: _____

E. Zev, the newborn elephant, weighs 267 pounds.
    Rex, the giraffe calf, weighs 158 pounds. Dov,
    the baby sea lion, weighs 45 pounds. How much
    do the elephant and giraffe weigh together?

Answer: _____

Name _____

Adding three-digit numbers. Three-place regrouping to the 1000's. Subtraction practice.

A.	835 + 251	632 + 849	628 − 179	337 + 276	982 − 438
B.	486 + 695	207 − 135	637 − 381	268 + 727	579 + 725
C.	835 + 838	737 − 149	823 + 557	880 − 677	961 − 602
D.	509 − 315	945 + 473	182 + 445	967 − 742	577 + 935
E.	556 + 266	762 − 493	808 − 484	763 + 279	576 + 483
F.	719 + 461	774 + 375	941 − 224	441 + 898	371 − 189

     Addition and Subtraction: Beyond Math Facts   **43**

Name _____

Addition and subtraction practice. Regrouping.

A.
```
   228        771        839        942        588
 - 187      + 859      + 669      - 549      + 272
```

B.
```
   920        822        745        309        597
 - 148      + 426      - 359      - 126      + 883
```

C.
```
   369        654        412        978        714
 - 277      - 475      - 354      - 481      + 618
```

Addition with money to the ten-dollar place. Regrouping. Subtraction money practice.

D.
```
  $7.60      $5.64      $6.13      $1.86      $8.37
 - 5.20     + 6.43     - 1.73     - 1.29     - 1.93
```

E.
```
  $4.47      $8.36      $7.36      $9.72      $6.96
 + 7.49     - 3.14     + 1.77     + 3.43     + 9.08
```

F.
```
  $2.50      $6.36      $2.55      $5.28      $3.98
 - 1.93     + 6.25     + 8.47     - 2.66     + 7.18
```

Addition and Subtraction: Beyond Math Facts

Name _____

Review addition and subtraction. One-place regrouping.

A.	243 + 538	174 − 46	942 + 84	211 − 150	465 − 28
B.	708 − 262	843 + 356	317 − 32	393 − 236	684 − 159
C.	548 − 485	290 − 24	980 − 367	611 + 552	459 − 378

Review addition and subtraction. Two-place regrouping.

D.	535 − 74	851 − 363	138 + 187	825 − 428	232 − 145
E.	914 − 61	682 + 237	814 − 648	859 − 81	921 − 188
F.	708 + 863	635 − 556	771 − 566	783 + 365	542 − 267

Name _____

Review addition. Three-place regrouping. Subtraction practice.

A. 585   983   139   361   265
   +532   +747   − 72   −138   +736

B. 848   463   490   697   712
   +725   −175   −226   +764   −667

C. 662   579   237   387   923
   − 88   −427   −144   +805   −557

D. 991   540   730   983   726
   −647   +760   −274   +288   −467

E. 277   491   666   197   334
   −195   −335   +458   +748   −236

F. 972   866   826   820   537
   +538   +361   − 55   −139   +387

Name _____

Review addition and subtraction. Regrouping.

A.	363 + 388	475 + 558	911 − 663	250 − 173	639 − 163
B.	427 − 258	279 + 363	751 − 466	962 − 207	886 + 732
C.	893 − 696	619 − 384	586 + 395	857 + 622	620 − 546

Review addition and subtraction, including money. Regrouping.

D.	$4.74 + 8.27	$7.55 − 3.47	272 − 194	681 − 228	$9.31 + 9.83
E.	152 + 692	323 − 239	$7.38 + 3.43	$3.58 − 2.86	712 − 525
F.	$8.10 − 5.54	$4.96 − 2.18	533 − 378	538 + 772	$9.84 − 7.78

Addition and Subtraction: Beyond Math Facts **47**

Name _____

Review addition and subtraction. Regrouping.

A.
$$751 - 385$$
$$984 - 145$$
$$528 - 183$$
$$886 + 315$$
$$325 + 972$$

B.
$$961 + 674$$
$$943 - 392$$
$$324 + 758$$
$$782 - 318$$
$$680 - 348$$

C.
$$464 - 197$$
$$277 + 743$$
$$906 - 234$$
$$829 - 146$$
$$589 + 635$$

D.
$$852 - 771$$
$$133 + 368$$
$$575 + 895$$
$$931 - 482$$
$$718 + 586$$

E.
$$715 - 143$$
$$690 - 566$$
$$296 + 589$$
$$335 + 834$$
$$531 - 269$$

F.
$$371 + 539$$
$$579 + 617$$
$$739 - 362$$
$$453 + 748$$
$$944 - 778$$

Name _____

Subtracting with three-digit numbers. Two-place regrouping and zero.

A.
$$
\begin{array}{r} 8\ 9 \\ 9\cancel{0}\cancel{1}5 \\ -\ 118 \\ \hline 7 \end{array}
$$

$$
\begin{array}{r} 301 \\ -292 \\ \hline \end{array}
$$

$$
\begin{array}{r} 604 \\ -165 \\ \hline \end{array}
$$

$$
\begin{array}{r} 103 \\ -\ 40 \\ \hline \end{array}
$$

$$
\begin{array}{r} 401 \\ -295 \\ \hline \end{array}
$$

B.
$$
\begin{array}{r} 203 \\ -\ 73 \\ \hline \end{array}
$$

$$
\begin{array}{r} 702 \\ -255 \\ \hline \end{array}
$$

$$
\begin{array}{r} 990 \\ -258 \\ \hline \end{array}
$$

$$
\begin{array}{r} 209 \\ -107 \\ \hline \end{array}
$$

$$
\begin{array}{r} 916 \\ -684 \\ \hline \end{array}
$$

C.
$$
\begin{array}{r} 504 \\ -347 \\ \hline \end{array}
$$

$$
\begin{array}{r} 800 \\ -137 \\ \hline \end{array}
$$

$$
\begin{array}{r} 503 \\ -\ 17 \\ \hline \end{array}
$$

$$
\begin{array}{r} 847 \\ -285 \\ \hline \end{array}
$$

$$
\begin{array}{r} 703 \\ -305 \\ \hline \end{array}
$$

Addition and subtraction practice. Regrouping.

D.
$$
\begin{array}{r} 400 \\ -171 \\ \hline \end{array}
$$

$$
\begin{array}{r} 708 \\ +496 \\ \hline \end{array}
$$

$$
\begin{array}{r} 512 \\ -238 \\ \hline \end{array}
$$

$$
\begin{array}{r} 905 \\ -397 \\ \hline \end{array}
$$

$$
\begin{array}{r} 489 \\ +334 \\ \hline \end{array}
$$

E.
$$
\begin{array}{r} 231 \\ +590 \\ \hline \end{array}
$$

$$
\begin{array}{r} 625 \\ -372 \\ \hline \end{array}
$$

$$
\begin{array}{r} 385 \\ +845 \\ \hline \end{array}
$$

$$
\begin{array}{r} 221 \\ -194 \\ \hline \end{array}
$$

$$
\begin{array}{r} 605 \\ -529 \\ \hline \end{array}
$$

F.
$$
\begin{array}{r} 630 \\ -493 \\ \hline \end{array}
$$

$$
\begin{array}{r} 504 \\ -486 \\ \hline \end{array}
$$

$$
\begin{array}{r} 737 \\ +672 \\ \hline \end{array}
$$

$$
\begin{array}{r} 891 \\ -745 \\ \hline \end{array}
$$

$$
\begin{array}{r} 700 \\ -616 \\ \hline \end{array}
$$

Name _____

Addition and subtraction practice. Regrouping.

A.
$$407 - 269$$
$$224 + 958$$
$$760 - 244$$
$$865 - 476$$
$$339 + 188$$

B.
$$551 + 261$$
$$204 - 132$$
$$708 + 855$$
$$602 - 103$$
$$247 + 896$$

C.
$$929 - 359$$
$$321 - 273$$
$$806 - 472$$
$$137 + 423$$
$$800 - 556$$

D.
$$586 - 363$$
$$874 + 822$$
$$493 - 174$$
$$644 - 66$$
$$729 - 455$$

E.
$$659 + 841$$
$$600 - 272$$
$$912 - 187$$
$$758 + 977$$
$$485 + 723$$

F.
$$862 + 393$$
$$224 + 766$$
$$676 + 773$$
$$900 - 859$$
$$705 - 698$$

50   Addition and Subtraction: Beyond Math Facts

Name _____

Adding and subtracting with four- and three-digit numbers. Three-place regrouping.

A.
```
  8616        4198        6667        1676        2967
-  332       -  414      -  796      +  168      +  834
```

B.
```
  1121        5553        3009        8874        6470
-  359       +  738      -  926      +  324      -  945
```

C.
```
  9068        7009        3534        2007        1589
+  754       -  745      +  955      -  895      +  862
```

Adding and subtracting, including money to the ten-dollar place. Regrouping.

D.
```
 $49.57       5796       $10.13       8847       $31.17
-  8.22      +  274      -  3.16     -  463      + 8.95
```

E.
```
  7081       $80.00      $74.02      $43.59       5293
-  627       -  2.70     -  8.35     + 7.26      +  335
```

F.
```
 $23.72       6571       $92.00       9136       $29.96
+  4.85      -  815      -  2.75     +  576      + 9.57
```

Addition and Subtraction: Beyond Math Facts   **51**

Name _____

Addition and subtraction practice. Regrouping.

A. 5008 − 189   3484 + 973   1012 − 996   4318 + 673   6825 + 177

B. 1019 − 147   2740 − 853   7585 + 466   6154 − 963   8407 + 846

C. 9009 − 612   3443 + 649   4593 + 114   2098 − 147   8782 + 551

D. 3272 + 489   8665 + 347   6071 − 713   9328 − 746   1868 + 479

E. 7668 − 471   5226 + 687   8821 + 556   5982 − 589   4123 − 277

F. 1668 + 583   4722 + 597   2017 − 462   7270 − 387   3685 + 879

Name _____

Adding and subtracting with four-digit numbers. Three-place regrouping.

A.	$\begin{array}{r} 2441 \\ -\ 1314 \\ \hline \end{array}$	$\begin{array}{r} 4218 \\ -\ 3927 \\ \hline \end{array}$	$\begin{array}{r} 3671 \\ +\ 2957 \\ \hline \end{array}$	$\begin{array}{r} 5735 \\ +\ 2188 \\ \hline \end{array}$	$\begin{array}{r} 9062 \\ -\ 1766 \\ \hline \end{array}$

B.	$\begin{array}{r} 6428 \\ +\ 3149 \\ \hline \end{array}$	$\begin{array}{r} 7589 \\ -\ 1748 \\ \hline \end{array}$	$\begin{array}{r} 6042 \\ -\ 1999 \\ \hline \end{array}$	$\begin{array}{r} 6615 \\ +\ 2866 \\ \hline \end{array}$	$\begin{array}{r} 8349 \\ -\ 7572 \\ \hline \end{array}$

C.	$\begin{array}{r} 4848 \\ +\ 2778 \\ \hline \end{array}$	$\begin{array}{r} 3468 \\ +\ 4671 \\ \hline \end{array}$	$\begin{array}{r} 7000 \\ -\ 2648 \\ \hline \end{array}$	$\begin{array}{r} 2287 \\ +\ 2658 \\ \hline \end{array}$	$\begin{array}{r} 4932 \\ +\ 4410 \\ \hline \end{array}$

Addition and subtraction practice, including money. Regrouping.

D.	$\begin{array}{r} \$11.96 \\ -\ 8.74 \\ \hline \end{array}$	$\begin{array}{r} 8772 \\ +\ 738 \\ \hline \end{array}$	$\begin{array}{r} \$13.74 \\ +\ 57.93 \\ \hline \end{array}$	$\begin{array}{r} \$92.85 \\ -\ 52.69 \\ \hline \end{array}$	$\begin{array}{r} 3081 \\ -\ 2983 \\ \hline \end{array}$

E.	$\begin{array}{r} 3864 \\ +\ 409 \\ \hline \end{array}$	$\begin{array}{r} \$28.38 \\ +\ 33.56 \\ \hline \end{array}$	$\begin{array}{r} \$84.93 \\ -\ 48.07 \\ \hline \end{array}$	$\begin{array}{r} \$52.10 \\ -\ 16.47 \\ \hline \end{array}$	$\begin{array}{r} 5842 \\ +\ 3259 \\ \hline \end{array}$

F.	$\begin{array}{r} \$90.68 \\ -\ 66.85 \\ \hline \end{array}$	$\begin{array}{r} 7895 \\ -\ 5352 \\ \hline \end{array}$	$\begin{array}{r} \$31.79 \\ +\ 62.23 \\ \hline \end{array}$	$\begin{array}{r} 1515 \\ +\ 8417 \\ \hline \end{array}$	$\begin{array}{r} \$96.78 \\ -\ 87.22 \\ \hline \end{array}$

Name _____

Addition and subtraction practice. Regrouping.

A.
$$1872 + 1245$$
$$9153 - 5257$$
$$2000 - 1507$$
$$8020 - 5330$$
$$6646 + 1583$$

B.
$$7441 - 5624$$
$$5797 + 316$$
$$2658 + 6403$$
$$4045 - 3847$$
$$3564 + 1267$$

C.
$$6235 - 2558$$
$$8386 - 7659$$
$$4387 + 3672$$
$$6001 - 3926$$
$$4663 + 5287$$

D.
$$5923 + 1233$$
$$6072 - 4844$$
$$3477 + 5275$$
$$9900 - 3566$$
$$4184 - 798$$

E.
$$3117 - 1181$$
$$4755 + 1879$$
$$8892 - 265$$
$$7538 + 884$$
$$2159 + 1933$$

F.
$$7451 + 1363$$
$$8009 - 3597$$
$$9423 - 8978$$
$$3559 + 3589$$
$$3806 + 2617$$

Name _____

Word Math. Solve the problems.   Show your work.

A. The Green Line Ferry holds 1,486 passengers, and the Wald Ferry Line holds 1,938 passengers. What is the total number of passengers the two ferries can hold?

Answer: _____

B. Sun School has 1,988 students. Moon School has 4,001 students, and Star Elementary has 3,196 students. How many more students does Moon School have than Sun School?

Answer: _____

C. Julie knows that a female hippopotamus weighs about 3,000 pounds and a male hippopotamus weighs about 7,000 pounds. If a giraffe can weigh 2,400 pounds, what is the difference in weight between the male hippopotamus and the giraffe?

Answer: _____

D. Jamie spent $3.10 for a drink and $8.05 for a movie ticket. How much money does she have left from a $20 bill?

Answer: _____

E. Erica has to save $80 to buy a new tennis racquet. She earned a total of $46.75 babysitting, and her grandma gave her $25 for her birthday. How much more money does she need to save?

Answer: _____

Record-Keeping Chart

Skill	Workbook Page	Description	Pre-Assessment Score Date _____	Post-Assessment Score Date _____
A	1	Adding two- and one-digit numbers.	□□ + ___ /2	□□ + ___ /2
A	2	Subtracting with two- and one-digit numbers.	□□ + ___ /2	□ + ___ /1
B	4	Adding two-digit numbers.	□□ + ___ /2	□ + ___ /1
B	4	Subtracting with two-digit numbers.	□□ + ___ /2	□□ + ___ /2
C	7	Adding two- and one-digit numbers. Regrouping to the 10's.	□□ + ___ /2	□ + ___ /1
D	11	Subtracting with two- and one-digit numbers. Regrouping.	□□ + ___ /2	□□ + ___ /2
E	15	Adding two-digit numbers. Regrouping to the 100's.	□□ + ___ /2	□□ + ___ /2
F	20	Adding two-digit numbers. Regrouping to the 10's.	□□ + ___ /2	□□ + ___ /2
G	23	Subtracting with two-digit numbers. Regrouping.	□□ + ___ /2	□□□ + ___ /3
H	25	Adding two-digit numbers. Two-place regrouping.	□□ + ___ /2	□□ + ___ /2
I	29	Adding and subtracting with three- and two-digit numbers. One-place regrouping.	□□□□□ + ___ /5	□□□□ + ___ /4
J	32	Adding and subtracting with money to the dollar place. One-place regrouping.	□□ + ___ /2	□□ + ___ /2
K	33	Adding three- and two-digit numbers. Two-place regrouping.	□□ + ___ /2	□□□ + ___ /3
L	37	Subtracting with three- and two-digit numbers. Two-place regrouping.	□□ + ___ /2	□□ + ___ /2
M	39	Adding and subtracting with three-digit numbers. One-place regrouping.	□□□□ + ___ /4	□□□□ + ___ /4
N	40	Adding and subtracting with three-digit numbers. Two-place regrouping.	□□□ + ___ /3	□□ + ___ /2
O	41	Adding and subtracting with money to the dollar place. Two-place regrouping.	□□ + ___ /2	□□ + ___ /2
P	43	Adding three-digit numbers. Three-place regrouping to the 1000's.	□ + ___ /1	□ + ___ /1
Q	44	Adding with money to the ten-dollar place. Three-place regrouping.	□ + ___ /1	□ + ___ /1
R	49	Subtracting with three-digit numbers. Two-place regrouping and zero.	□□ + ___ /2	□□ + ___ /2
S	51	Adding and subtracting with four- and three-digit numbers. Three-place regrouping.	□□ + ___ /2	□□□□ + ___ /4
T	53	Adding and subtracting with four-digit numbers. Three-place regrouping.	□□□ + ___ /3	□□□□ + ___ /4
U	53	Subtracting with money to the ten-dollar place. Three-place regrouping.	□ + ___ /1	□ + ___ /1

Pre-Assessment Part A

Name _____   Date _____

A.   24
   + 3

B.   51
   + 36

A.   85
   − 4

D.   63
   − 8

B.   98
   − 10

F.   77
   + 17

E.   26
   + 83

C.   66
   + 4

F.   35
   + 28

J. $7.94
   − .87

M. 287
   + 708

A.   57
   − 3

B.   98
   − 62

G.   70
   − 39

I.   246
   + 46

H.   73
   + 59

C.   39
   + 7

N. 652
   − 166

A.   96
   + 2

G.   91
   − 53

B.   43
   + 23

D.   40
   − 5

I.   295
   + 82

J. $6.40
   + .97

I.   570
   − 56

Pre-Assessment Part B

Name _____   Date _____

N. 930 − 643	H. 48 + 76	T. $26.96 + 68.19	L. 131 − 34	K. 553 + 67
M. 697 + 192	K. 425 + 97	S. 3453 − 587	I. 648 − 97	R. 800 − 424
T. 2437 + 5854	M. 529 − 474	Q. $6.38 + 7.64	O. $3.89 + 4.35	L. 916 − 77
O. $8.42 − 2.98	E. 84 + 85	T. 8009 − 6387	M. 981 − 856	P. 758 + 992
R. 705 − 458	S. 1573 + 468	N. 186 + 175	I. 247 − 29	U. $79.22 − 29.85

Post-Assessment Part A

Name _____   Date _____

A. $\begin{array}{r} 79 \\ -\ 3 \\ \hline \end{array}$ B. $\begin{array}{r} 32 \\ +36 \\ \hline \end{array}$ A. $\begin{array}{r} 55 \\ +\ 4 \\ \hline \end{array}$ D. $\begin{array}{r} 36 \\ -\ 9 \\ \hline \end{array}$ E. $\begin{array}{r} 71 \\ +47 \\ \hline \end{array}$

F. $\begin{array}{r} 28 \\ +47 \\ \hline \end{array}$ G. $\begin{array}{r} 73 \\ -54 \\ \hline \end{array}$ H. $\begin{array}{r} 39 \\ +79 \\ \hline \end{array}$ B. $\begin{array}{r} 49 \\ -32 \\ \hline \end{array}$ I. $\begin{array}{r} 443 \\ +\ 76 \\ \hline \end{array}$

C. $\begin{array}{r} 56 \\ +\ 8 \\ \hline \end{array}$ B. $\begin{array}{r} 86 \\ -36 \\ \hline \end{array}$ M. $\begin{array}{r} 609 \\ +238 \\ \hline \end{array}$ I. $\begin{array}{r} 862 \\ -\ 37 \\ \hline \end{array}$ J. $\begin{array}{r} \$2.25 \\ +\ .36 \\ \hline \end{array}$

J. $\begin{array}{r} \$4.09 \\ -\ .45 \\ \hline \end{array}$ M. $\begin{array}{r} 849 \\ -366 \\ \hline \end{array}$ G. $\begin{array}{r} 96 \\ -38 \\ \hline \end{array}$ K. $\begin{array}{r} 206 \\ +\ 97 \\ \hline \end{array}$ L. $\begin{array}{r} 533 \\ -\ 66 \\ \hline \end{array}$

F. $\begin{array}{r} 48 \\ +35 \\ \hline \end{array}$ K. $\begin{array}{r} 185 \\ +\ 29 \\ \hline \end{array}$ I. $\begin{array}{r} 917 \\ -\ 24 \\ \hline \end{array}$ I. $\begin{array}{r} 229 \\ +\ 52 \\ \hline \end{array}$ A. $\begin{array}{r} 65 \\ +\ 3 \\ \hline \end{array}$

Post-Assessment Part B

Name _____ Date _____

O. $9.24
   − 4.98

M.   692
   − 579

K.   247
   + 63

O. $3.41
   + 1.59

N.   358
   + 369

N.   513
   − 215

H.   84
   + 68

R.   805
   − 166

S. 1967
   + 645

U. $81.20
   − 39.57

T. $47.75
   + 12.95

D.   41
   −   7

Q. $7.57
   + 8.86

S. 8718
   + 743

R.   500
   − 448

S. 8014
   − 735

L.   415
   − 27

T. 3531
   + 4788

M.   582
   + 142

P.   892
   + 839

T. 9162
   − 1594

S. 7854
   − 882

E.   92
   + 47

T. 6378
   − 2879

G.   94
   − 67

Answers

Page 1
A. 76 43 26 10 68 98
B. 15 58 24 86 73 6
C. 10 27 65 10 10 39
D. 88 34 8 93 56 66
E. 67 18 55 6 19 10
F. 47 8 84 21 98 72

Page 2
A. 28 82 1 41 57 91
B. 1 76 23 11 9 21
C. 91 5 41 3 84 17
D. 72 52 31 14 81 2
E. 45 61 21 78 1 34
F. 5 51 62 93 33 71

Page 3
A. 38 11 83 24 95 1
B. 79 26 12 94 41 17
C. 65 74 31 10 56 61
D. 52 34 10 96 66 48
E. 48 54 9 71 10 81
F. 85 10 28 58 32 5

Page 4
A. 86 43 67 45 88 77
B. 68 98 58 97 66 59
C. 34 56 89 46 92 84
D. 11 46 18 12 13 15
E. 17 81 34 63 11 21
F. 53 41 31 71 14 12

Page 5
A. 46 88 21 1 74 43
B. 4 44 86 54 61 96
C. 68 74 10 31 93 15
D. 11 12 36 10 21 84
E. 75 80 17 91 68 5
F. 66 31 10 18 81 83

Page 6
A. 67 pages
B. 21 pictures
C. 13 cupcakes
D. 14 friends
E. 38 chairs

Page 7
A. 28 29 30 40 18 60
B. 33 80 46 60 90 98
C. 20 46 37 82 70 25
D. 76 50 68 30 43 36
E. 49 5 70 90 91 19
F. 63 20 92 72 96 51

Page 8
A. 44 31 80 89 53 37
B. 9 60 48 76 61 40
C. 87 88 96 48 51 68
D. 20 66 86 41 1 82
E. 28 58 11 44 13 57
F. 86 20 50 5 90 36

Page 9
A. 32 77 36 55 94 45
B. 90 97 30 80 31 17
C. 53 82 18 26 50 25
D. 64 74 78 70 6 47
E. 91 72 92 45 34 98
F. 50 7 56 40 88 60

Page 10
A. 94 33 7 38 27 65
B. 84 45 51 78 20 61
C. 58 70 27 10 44 31
D. 1 42 81 86 48 76
E. 72 95 37 20 21 90
F. 75 81 88 12 36 58

Page 11
A. 71 40 29 46 51 35
B. 11 81 20 57 22 69
C. 62 88 33 24 31 34
D. 55 86 90 85 21 48
E. 75 37 61 56 30 58
F. 59 97 67 20 42 75

Page 12
A. 20 95 65 30 91 50
B. 17 96 36 81 70 58
C. 41 47 68 26 52 57
D. 85 10 26 38 21 90
E. 64 42 47 76 83 89
F. 51 24 66 50 87 63

Page 13
A. 91 80 39 16 88 61
B. 15 2 52 89 27 46
C. 68 65 93 28 55 30
D. 36 94 90 79 50 42
E. 78 87 86 51 71 67
F. 65 15 19 22 87 47

Page 14
A. $41
B. 40 children
C. 34 minutes
D. 37 points
E. 87 minutes

Page 15
A. 95 106 146 156 107 184
B. 137 48 87 128 141 75
C. 109 178 68 163 85 105
D. 103 46 115 106 12 77
E. 128 72 149 14 19 41
F. 25 30 174 2 108 11

Page 16
A. 108 67 132 51 41 11
B. 184 58 42 156 177 148
C. 75 21 55 3 82 107
D. 29 87 1 104 31 166
E. 118 17 100 146 38 128
F. 105 85 73 107 76 5

Page 17
A. 76 33 33 39 57 18
B. 56 92 139 44 38 62
C. 69 20 25 99 40 97
D. 58 33 168 63 36 98
E. 108 81 95 44 34 56
F. 13 138 88 15 48 53

Page 18
A. 33 155 139 87 56 24
B. 39 75 40 126 34 30
C. 62 15 52 22 39 16
D. 109 23 88 43 136 119
E. 25 63 149 70 48 56
F. 45 65 68 81 38 146

Page 19
A. 6 8 7 10 8 13
B. 14 18 11 9 15 9
C. 10 10 8 11 14 17
D. 11 19 17 10 10 14

Page 20
A. 33 83 148 74 34 164
B. 98 59 94 90 168 70
C. 99 65 105 63 109 86
D. 90 98 40 127 90 33
E. 71 10 139 32 53 96
F. 64 92 135 60 177 46

Page 21
A. 74 138 42 109 58 65
B. 36 94 63 129 21 82
C. 51 3 95 30 149 48
D. 159 50 29 34 90 31
E. 91 105 63 56 37 89
F. 82 65 83 88 136 16

Page 22
A. 35 99 165 53 33 80
B. 54 18 57 83 56 187
C. 166 70 98 68 31 16
D. 86 3 60 45 63 89
E. 109 14 78 33 79 58
F. 98 148 96 79 42 94

Page 23
A. 12 35 51 68 31 9
B. 46 7 43 68 33 45
C. 18 85 26 11 64 47
D. 37 149 16 188 14 129
E. 53 19 35 65 90 138
F. 9 76 109 37 107 62

Page 24
A. 97 69 86 106 57 8
B. 36 95 40 11 159 3
C. 16 138 25 60 15 148
D. 94 43 53 8 179 79
E. 58 92 6 189 69 90
F. 166 35 158 93 32 25

Page 25
A. 83 111 140 164 70 173
B. 90 137 196 171 142 116
C. 129 60 110 155 99 107
D. 113 174 28 36 55 18
E. 137 27 13 38 99 6
F. 53 63 45 179 21 14

Page 26
A. 106 tables
B. 5 students
C. 130 children
D. $33
E. 48 miles

Page 27
A. 61 100 44 129 91 133
B. 157 118 140 92 154 101
C. 82 108 69 146 113 74
D. 9 8 19 7 53 49
E. 15 33 4 46 35 4
F. 49 56 29 38 19 32

Page 28
A. 149 39 45 4 120 24
B. 72 19 75 107 9 141
C. 37 104 92 45 27 147
D. 51 114 171 19 124 136
E. 58 69 125 32 68 49
F. 93 4 16 9 120 27

Page 29
A. 151 484 342 424 325
B. 916 762 887 618 209
C. 553 131 237 792 297
D. 661 593 245 939 694
E. 353 768 163 396 438
F. 660 572 816 804 960

Page 30
A. 409 848 683 568 894
B. 318 476 425 744 992
C. 884 235 587 689 949
D. 343 451 637 219 854
E. 873 166 728 94 697
F. 215 262 619 293 840

Page 31
A. 304 444 983 696 944
B. 806 249 473 365 849
C. 629 723 198 693 791
D. 782 384 108 393 264
E. 411 991 350 376 473
F. 314 392 708 728 559

Page 32
A. $8.25 $2.18 $8.17 $3.16
$4.84
B. $1.95 $1.81 $9.94 $7.25
$3.35
C. $5.76 $3.91 $1.85 $3.38
$5.53
D. $8.19 454 674 $6.38 905
E. 429 $0.41 392 $9.22 649
F. 299 $4.12 809 844 $5.80

Page 33
A. 338 412 406 460 854
B. 444 223 381 902 634
C. 382 898 560 371 613
D. 654 344 594 663 933
E. 575 308 573 552 684
F. 337 250 592 916 914

Page 34
A. 184 614 532 144 735
B. 530 852 368 453 156
C. 608 375 966 542 109
D. 538 908 463 396 208
E. 729 521 867 292 675
F. 839 412 894 694 714

Page 35
A. 209 children
B. $6.22
C. 200 miles
D. 54 centimeters
E. 316 cars

Page 36
A. 862 559 956 311 122
B. 872 431 523 984 645
C. 837 492 205 352 824
D. 220 479 114 760 217
E. 722 868 533 125 617
F. 477 972 632 300 752

Page 37
A. 939 283 567 392 539
B. 870 847 657 927 408
C. 838 113 691 799 442
D. 625 309 243 227 958
E. 774 355 623 499 540
F. 310 192 923 723 401

Page 38
A. 82 446 947 319 785
B. 512 759 285 295 751
C. 923 246 174 634 332
D. $6.51 $7.94 226 800 $3.62
E. 858 $3.87 $1.80 $2.29 586
F. $3.49 911 927 $5.45 $6.03

Page 39
A. 623 972 251 610 354
B. 961 358 577 292 858
C. 263 502 158 472 675
D. 847 949 83 926 960
E. 429 795 281 383 229
F. 939 643 196 472 969

Page 40
A. 372 929 915 653 813
B. 584 991 631 540 918
C. 850 823 859 948 985
D. 617 18 198 578 125
E. 249 402 242 247 736
F. 429 127 479 589 732

Page 41
A. 76 545 437 976 445
B. 375 450 77 362 711
C. 741 85 382 710 188
D. $1.31 $1.92 327 980 $2.12
E. 929 657 $4.44 $3.32 554
F. $6.15 $8.19 973 811 $2.25

Page 42
A. 42 pounds
B. 32 cents
C. $2.00
D. 933 candy bars
E. 425 pounds

Page 43
A. 1,086 1,481 449 613 544
B. 1,181 72 256 995 1,304
C. 1,673 588 1,380 203 359
D. 194 1,418 627 225 1,512
E. 822 269 324 1,042 1,059
F. 1,180 1,149 717 1,339 182

Page 44
A. 41 1,630 1,508 393 860
B. 772 1,248 386 183 1,480
C. 92 179 58 497 1,332
D. $2.40 $12.07 $4.40 $0.57 $6.44
E. $11.96 $5.22 $9.13 $13.15 $16.04
F. $0.57 $12.61 $11.02 $2.62 $11.16

Page 45
A. 781 128 1,026 61 437
B. 446 1,199 285 157 525
C. 63 266 613 1,163 81
D. 461 488 325 397 87
E. 853 919 166 778 733
F. 1,571 79 205 1,148 275

Page 46
A. 1,117 1,730 67 223 1,001
B. 1,573 288 264 1,461 45
C. 574 152 93 1,192 366
D. 344 1,300 456 1,271 259
E. 82 156 1,124 945 98
F. 1,510 1,227 771 681 924

Page 47
A. 751 1,033 248 77 476
B. 169 642 285 755 1,618
C. 197 235 981 1,479 74
D. $13.01 $4.08 78 453 $19.14
E. 844 84 $10.81 $0.72 187
F. $2.56 $2.78 155 1,310 $2.06

Page 48
A. 366 839 345 1,201 1,297
B. 1,635 551 1,082 464 332
C. 267 1,020 672 683 1,224
D. 81 501 1,470 449 1,304
E. 572 124 885 1,169 262
F. 910 1,196 377 1,201 166

Page 49
A. 787 9 439 63 106
B. 130 447 732 102 232
C. 157 663 486 562 398
D. 229 1,204 274 508 823
E. 821 253 1,230 27 76
F. 137 18 1,409 146 84

Page 50
A. 138 1,182 516 389 527
B. 812 72 1,563 499 1,143
C. 570 48 334 560 244
D. 223 1,696 319 578 274
E. 1,500 328 725 1,735 1,208
F. 1,255 990 1,449 41 7

Page 51
A. 8,284 3,784 5,871 1,844 3,801
B. 762 6,291 2,083 9,198 5,525
C. 9,822 6,264 4,489 1,112 2,451
D. $41.35 6,070 $6.97 8,384 $40.12
E. 6,454 $77.30 $65.67 5,085 5,628
F. $28.57 5,756 $89.25 9,712 $39.53

Page 52
A. 4,819 4,457 16 4,991 7,002
B. 872 1,887 8,051 5,191 9,253
C. 8,397 4,092 4,707 1,951 9,333
D. 3,761 9,012 5,358 8,582 2,347
E. 7,197 5,913 9,377 5,393 3,846
F. 2,251 5,319 1,555 6,883 4,564

Page 53
A. 1,127 291 6,628 7,923 7,296
B. 9,577 5,841 4,043 9,481 777
C. 7,626 8,139 4,352 4,945 9,342
D. $3.22 9,510 $71.67 $40.16 98
E. 4,273 $61.94 $36.86 $35.63 9,101
F. $23.83 2,543 $94.02 9,932 $9.56

Page 54
A. 3,117 3,896 493 2,690 8,229
B. 1,817 6,113 9,061 198 4,831
C. 3,677 727 8,059 2,075 9,950
D. 7,156 1,228 8,752 6,334 3,386
E. 1,936 6,634 8,627 8,422 4,092
F. 8,814 4,412 445 7,148 6,423

Page 55
A. 3,424 passengers
B. 2,013 students
C. 4,600 pounds
D. $8.85
E. $8.25

Page 57 Pre-Assessment Part A
27 87 81 55 88
94 109 70 63 $7.07
995 54 36 31 292
132 46 486 98 38
66 35 377 $7.37 514

Page 58 Pre-Assessment Part B
287 124 $95.15 97 620
889 522 2,866 551 376
8,291 55 $14.02 $8.24 839
$5.44 169 1,622 125 1,750
247 2,041 361 218 $49.37

Page 59 Post-Assessment Part A
76 68 59 27 118
75 19 118 17 519
64 50 847 825 $2.61
$3.64 483 58 303 467
83 214 893 281 68

Page 60 Post-Assessment Part B
$4.26 113 310 $5.00 727
298 152 639 2,612 $41.63
$60.70 34 $16.43 9,461 52
7,279 388 8,319 724 1,731
7,568 6,972 139 3,499 27